THE CABINET OF NATURAL HISTORY
AND
AMERICAN RURAL SPORTS

THE CABINET of NATURAL HISTORY AND AMERICAN RURAL SPORTS With ILLUSTRATIONS.

Edited by GAIL STEWART

Introduction by WILSON G. DUPREY

IMPRINT SOCIETY

Barre, Massachusetts

1973

77383
IMP

CONTENTS

VOLUME II

VOLUME III

INTRODUCTION

The following advertisement appeared in the *National Gazette* of Philadelphia on November 2, 1830:

The Cabinet of Natural History and American Rural Sports

The subscribers are about issuing a Periodical under the title *Cabinet of Natural History and American Rural Sports*, the object of which is to embrace the Natural History of this country in the higher and more interesting branches of Zoology, viz: Ornithology and Mammalogy, together with an account of the Sports and Pastimes of North America.

No work of this kind, we believe, has yet appeared before the American public; and as the knowledge of the Natural History of this country is confined to but few individuals, yet it is a subject calculated for much instruction, and well worthy the attention of all persons desirous of obtaining useful and extensive knowledge; and considering the very low price at which this work will be issued, it is confidently hoped that liberal encouragement will be given to the publishers, and their motives for disseminating useful information, justly appreciated.

The Cabinet of Natural History and American Rural Sports will be issued monthly, in a quarto form, and printed with new type on fine royal paper. Each number will contain twenty-four pages, closely printed matter, and embellished with two beautiful coloured plates, of Birds and Quadrupeds, drawn from nature, and executed in the best style, with a perfect history of each object so represented. It will also contain many interesting Anecdotes, relating to Natural History, and all other subjects which may give interest, comportable with the spirit of the work, as connected with fishing, hunting, and shooting parties, the various clubs established for gymnastic exercises, aquatic sports &c.

The first number will be issued early in the month of November.

Terms, eight dollars per annum, payable in advance.

> John Doughty
> Thomas Doughty
> No. 80 Walnut St.

Such was the plan, and the publication proceeded until 1833, when it came to an abrupt end, probably due more to financial difficulties of the times than to anything else. In its final form the publication included, besides the text, fifty-six plates in twenty-eight parts, usually found today in three bound volumes dated 1830, 1832, 1833. Fifty-three of the plates are hand-colored lithographs, one plate is a hand-colored engraving, and two are black-and-white engravings. Volume I includes in addition a number of delightful wood-engravings in the text by Reuben S. Gilbert, nearly all dealing with the general subject of rural sports: skaters on the ice in winter, deer in a meadow, a hunter shooting quail with his dogs, a canoe and a hunter's shelter in the woods, a bear after honey in a hive. Each volume has an engraved title-page with a sporting scene as a vignette; the frontispiece to volume I is an engraved half-length portrait of Charles Willson Peale, and that to volume II an engraved half-length portrait of William Bartram.

The present Imprint edition in one volume retains all of the fifty-six plates, twelve in full color, and some of the wood-engravings. The text accompanying the plates has been abridged. The three title pages and the two frontispieces are included, as well as full biographical sketches of both Peale and Bartram from the original edition.

Charles Willson Peale had been a conspicuous figure in the world of painting, certainly the dean of American painters at the time, but he was also in the forefront in the field of natural history, with his Philadelphia Museum a standard fixture in the life of Philadelphia. William Bartram was the leading botanist of his day, a prominent local ornithologist, and a close friend of Alexander Wilson, the famous American specialist in ornithology. Both Peale and Bartram were probably known to the Doughty brothers, and no two men could have been more suitable to decorate and give significance to this pioneer publication.

Thomas Doughty, already an established and well-known painter by 1830, was often termed the father of American landscape painting. He was responsible for the twenty-four designs in the first volume, having drawn twenty-three of them on the lithographic stones himself. He had probably learned what he knew about lithography from the Pendletons in Boston, where he had painted in the years just prior to 1830. But he also knew Cephas G. Childs, a pioneer lithographer in Philadelphia, where the Doughtys originated. The partnership of the Doughty brothers was ended in May 1832, when Thomas resumed painting as a full time career and departed for Boston again.[1] John Doughty remained as the sole publisher. Other artists continued in the manner of Thomas Doughty, portraying each bird or animal against an appropriate landscape. The artists, among whom were M. E. D. Brown, J. G. Clonney, C. G. Childs, G. Lehman, and A. Rider, worked of course in the same form—colored lithographs. Most of the stones were printed by the Childs & Inman Press in Philadelphia, but curiously some of the stones were printed by E. S. Mesier, an early lithographer of New York, and others by Pendleton in Boston— all of which would indicate a rather close-knit fraternity among the practitioners of the new medium of lithography in the three major cities of the United States in 1832-1833. Although evidence is still too indefinite to fully document the establishment and development of the lithograph in the United States, it can be said that the new technique was fairly well established in Boston, New York, and Philadelphia by 1825.

Bibliographically speaking, *The Cabinet of Natural History and American Rural Sports* carries the distinction of being the first color plate sporting title published in the United States. There had been, of course, other color plate books prior to this period, perhaps the most important being William Birch's *Views of Philadelphia* (1800), Joshua Shaw's *Picturesque Views of American Scenery* (1820–21) with colored aquatints by John Hill,[2] and the *Hudson River Portfolio* (1820-25) with colored aquatints by John Hill after paintings mostly by William Guy Wall. The first two titles had been published in Philadelphia, the last one in New York. But with the *Cabinet* we have a new breed of publication, a most unusual combination in which colored lithographs are used to show a bird or animal against a backdrop of landscape. (Only six prints lack these backgrounds.) Although there had been in the United States earlier examples of book illustration with colored lithographs,[3] the *Cabinet* was probably the first successful venture with considerable distribution around the country. It was an important influence on the lithographic medium in publishing, for within a very short time numerous publications with colored lithographs were published, and of course separate lithographs in the form of portraits, views, sheet music covers, and political caricatures shortly flooded the scene.

The illustrations in the *Cabinet* depicted the regional and unusual birds and animals of the United States at that time— flamingo, pelican, buffalo, prairie wolf, mountain sheep—as well as the more widespread and familiar—turkey, robin, quail, jay, oriole, fox, squirrel, skunk, hawk, wren, blue bird, owl,

duck. As an extra treat, a plate displaying the eggs of twenty-three kinds of birds was added. One of the most striking illustrations, that of the *Wild Turkey*, may remind the reader of the one by John J. Audubon in *Birds of America*. However, M. E. D. Brown's bird seems of a much wilder strain, with brilliant plumage, and it is doubtful if Brown had seen the Audubon plate; at least he was not influenced by it.

Any naturalist looking at the description of each plate in the *Cabinet* was readily apprised of source materials in which he could pursue his interest further. Here are references to Linnaeus or Buffon and other publications for the most demanding specialist. Here also is the information as to where the artist found his specimen for drafting, alive or stuffed. Altogether there is evidence of numerous naturalists scattered around the country, many of whom collected specimens and maintained collections of stuffed birds and animals. Among these was the publisher himself, John Doughty, who provided the specimens for many of the drawings made by his brother Thomas for volume I. Other drawings were made from specimens in the Philadelphia Museum (Peale's museum), a few from life from the Menagerie of Living Animals which was exhibited in 1830-1832 in Philadelphia, and still others from private collections: those of S. P. Griffitts of Philadelphia and L. J. Salaignac of Charleston, South Carolina.

The editors searched out anecdotes and accounts from personal journals as well as pertinent excerpts from published sources such as *Long's Expedition*. Naturalists from various parts of the country were invited to contribute manuscripts, and comments from the aforementioned Salaignac of South Carolina and from James Eights of Albany, New York, were included as instances of regional accounts. The topics of the text ranged well beyond mere description of the plates, from the explosion of myths about beavers to the ways Indians hunt buffalo, how to kill large insects for mounting, and even how to straighten a bent feather. It is not surprising to find on one of the wrappers accompanying the *Cabinet* a list of establishments catering equipment to hunters and anglers, two in New York City, six in Philadelphia, and two in Rochester, New York, which in those days must have been considered quite near the wilderness. A taxidermist is also listed in New York City, one J. F. Ward, 93 Barclay Street.[4]

Despite growing financial and technological difficulties, Doughty contemplated the enlargement of his periodical by offering to include among the birds and animals examples of American trees, if encouraged to do so by subscribers.[5] He also had in mind a separate publication dealing with game birds.[6] From time to time, Doughty was able to make interesting announcements regarding the contents of an issue, rather than explanations for the delay of an issue. He proudly noted, for example, the inclusion of the swan and the pelican in the *Cabinet*, birds which he claimed had never been included in

Wilson or Buonaparte, standard works on ornithology.[7]

We do not know the size of the *Cabinet* edition, but in the eighth issue the publishers announced that the first edition had been disposed of sufficiently to pay for the work without profit and the editors proposed to strike off another 750 copies as remuneration before continuing the publication.[8] Early in the game, agencies had been set up in fifteen states to facilitate subscriptions: Maine, Massachusetts, Rhode Island, Connecticut, New York, New Jersey, Pennsylvania, Maryland, District of Columbia, Virginia, North Carolina, South Carolina, Tennessee, Kentucky, and Ohio.[9] In the more populated states there were agencies in various cities. All this seems reason to believe that the publication had rather widespread distribution. Nevertheless, today only the most prestigious public and private collections can exhibit a complete set of the publication.[10] The third volume is extremely rare. Single plates of the birds and animals appear from time to time, but they are not at all common.

By close comparison of the lithographs in different bound volumes, it has been discerned that a few of the stones were redrawn or reworked in later printings. It is of course possible that some of the stones were broken in the printing and had to be replaced. The publishers experienced numerous trials during the publication's short life, and obviously they were still in the pioneer stages of a new technology. There were shortages of quality paper, and one whole edition of plates was ruined when sent to be sized prior to coloring—to cite but two examples of the problems faced by the publishers as the specter of ruin came closer and closer. Although no evidence or specific statement has been found as to the reason for the *Cabinet*'s demise, technological problems added to the national banking and political upheavals in the year 1833 were probably enough to kill it. Subscriptions were not coming forth sufficiently to pay for the costs involved.

The importance of the *Cabinet* in the bibliography of natural history has yet to be assessed. A sizable buying public was needed, and thus the work's approach had to be somewhat popular. No doubt there were more subscribers among the city and country gentry than among the naturalists of the era. Nevertheless, its significance in the field of lithography is unquestioned: the *Cabinet* ranks high among the early successful examples of that art in America, and first among this country's colored sporting titles.

WILSON G. DUPREY
Curator of Prints, New-York Historical Society

The term "wrapper note" below refers to printed notices found on original wrappers covering or bound in with the parts as issued. The American Antiquarian Society has one of the few copies of the *Cabinet* with such wrappers intact. The Arents Collection copy at the New York Public Library has the original wrappers for volumes I and II only.

1. Wrapper note: vol. 2, nos. 3 and 4.

2. It is of interest to learn that John Sartain, certainly a well known name in the field of American prints, was invited to engrave the first plate in volume I—*Common Deer*, the only colored engraving in the publication. According to a manuscript biography by a descendant of Doughty in the New-York Historical Society, he had emigrated to the United States from England and had hardly stepped off the boat when he was invited to engrave the plate by Thomas Doughty in the company of Thomas T. Ash. Ash was the publisher of the reissue of Joshua Shaw's *Picturesque Views of American Scenery*, Philadelphia, 1835. This is an example of the intimate coterie of artists and publishers of the time.

3. James E. Smith, *Grammar of Botany....* New York, 1822. With 20 colored lithographs by Arthur J. Stansbury, printed by Barnet & Doolittle.
Peter Guillet, *Timber Merchant's Guide....* Baltimore, 1823. With 30 lithographs, colored, by Henry Stone.

4. Wrapper note: vol. 1, no. 11.

5. Wrapper note: vol. 3, no. 2.

6. Wrapper note: vol. 2, nos. 1–4. Publication was to have been titled *American feathered game, the grouse, pheasant, partridge, woodcock & snipe*, to sell for "one dollar twenty-five cents each plate."

7. Wrapper notes: vol. 1, nos. 8 and 2.

8. Wrapper note: vol. 1, no. 8.

9. Wrapper note: vol. 1, no. 3.

10. The following is a partial list of public collections in which copies of the *Cabinet* may be found; in many cases the third volume is lacking:

San Marino, California: Henry E. Huntington Library
New Haven, Connecticut: Beinecke Rare Book and
   Manuscript Library, Yale University
Washington, D.C.: Library of Congress
Chicago, Illinois: John Crerar Library
   University of Chicago
Lexington, Kentucky: University of Kentucky
Cambridge, Massachusetts: Harvard University
Worcester, Massachusetts: American Antiquarian
   Society
Albany, New York: New York State Library
New York, New York: Columbia University
   New-York Historical Society
   New York Public Library
West Point, New York: U.S. Military Academy
   Warner Collection
Philadelphia, Pennsylvania: Academy of Natural
   Sciences
   American Philosophical Society
   Free Library of Philadelphia
   Historical Society of Pennsylvania
   Library Company of Philadelphia
   University of Pennsylvania
Charlottesville, Virginia: University of Virginia

THE CABINET of Natural History,

AND American Rural Sports with ILLUSTRATIONS.

Vol. 1

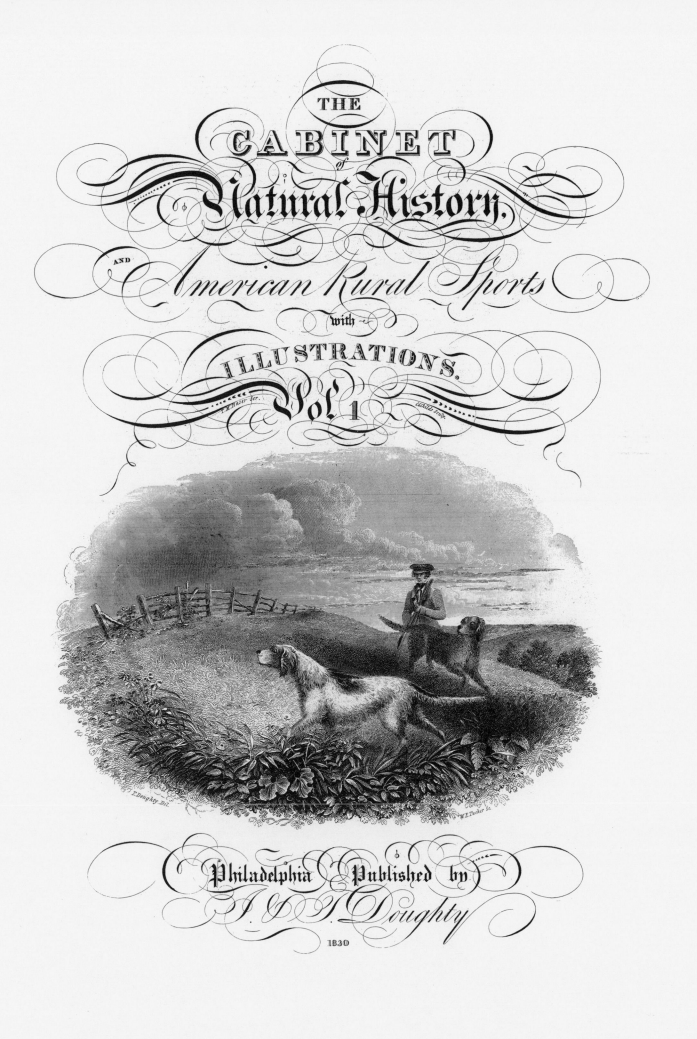

J.M.Naser Ser.   Childs Sculp.

T.Doughty Del.   W.E.Tucker Sc.

Philadelphia Published by
J. & T. Doughty

1830

C W Peale

Engraved by J.B. Longacre from an Original Painting by Rembrant Peale.

BIOGRAPHICAL SKETCH

OF

CHARLES WILLSON PEALE.

THE records of Natural History and of the Fine Arts in this country would be incomplete, without some notice of a man who was among the earliest to cultivate a taste for Painting, and the first to establish a Museum of Natural History, even when the name of Museum was scarcely recognized from the European dictionaries. It would require more time than we can now bestow, to perform this duty with the minuteness which might be desired. We will, therefore, content ourselves with a slight sketch of his varied career.

His father, Charles Peale, is still remembered by some of the oldest inhabitants of Maryland as a gentleman of liberal education and polite manners; greatly respected as a teacher at Chestertown, where he occasionally officiated in the pulpit, when the clergyman of the parish happened to be absent. He was a native of Rutlandshire in England; proud of the freedom which Britons enjoyed, but still prouder of the advantages which he foresaw were to be developed here. He died in the year 1750, leaving a widow and five children, of whom the eldest was Charles Willson, the subject of the present memoir; Margaret Jane, who first married a British officer, afterwards Colonel Nathaniel Ramsay; St. George, who was distinguished as the head of the Land Office; Elizabeth Digby, who married Captain Polk; and James, who has been long distinguished as a painter of miniatures and still life.

Charles Willson Peale was born at Chestertown, on the eastern shore of Maryland, April 16th, 1741. At an early age he was bound apprentice to a saddler in Annapolis; and the habits of industry which he acquired under the obligations of that servitude, gave a character to the labours of his whole life, to which was added a perseverance from his own peculiar temperament, which seemed to delight in conquering difficulties.

He was married before he was twenty-one years of age, and for several years carried on the business of his apprenticeship; to which he successively added coach, clock and watch making, and something of the silversmith business.

But this variety of occupation, though it amused the eager and volatile fancy of a youth of very sanguine temperament, instead of advancing his interest, only accumulated around him embarrassments which distressed him for a long time.

Hitherto he had thought but little of drawing; yet he had copied some prints with a pen and ink, had coloured prints on glass, and even painted an Adam and Eve from the inspiration of Milton. It was on a visit to Norfolk, where he went to purchase leather, that seeing a portrait and some landscapes painted by a Mr. Frazier,—instead of being stimulated by a display of excellence to aspire to excellence in art—it was the badness of the performances which encouraged him in the idea of surpassing them. He therefore secretly procured some pigments and canvass from a coach maker, and soon surprised his friends by a landscape and portrait of himself, in which he was represented holding a palette and brushes in his hand, with a clock in the background. He never could remember to whom he had given this portrait, or where it had been mislaid, till forty years afterwards, it was discovered tied up as a bag, and containing a pound or two of whiting; having travelled, unopened, during the revolutionary struggles, from place to place. This picture immediately drew him into notice, and procured him employment, still further to the disadvantage of his original business.

His mind was now wholly bent on painting, and it was necessary to procure the proper materials for it. He had never seen an easel or palette, and knew only the most common colours which the coach painters then used. For this purpose he travelled to Philadelphia, which was then a journey of some fatigue and peril; and in the well furnished shop of Christopher Marshall, was bewildered by the variety of colours, the names of which he had never before heard. Some book on painting might relieve him from this embarrassment, and Rivington's bookstore furnished him with the "Handmaid to the Arts." This, in the solitude of his lodgings, he studied day and night for nearly a week, before he could venture upon the selection and purchase of

1

his paints, with which he hastened back to Annapolis, eager to commence.

Previous to this, there had been only three persons in Maryland, professing the art of portrait painting: Cain, Hesselius, and Woolaston. They were artists from the parent country, who had made profitable circuits through the colonies, furnishing to the most wealthy families laudable portraits and groups in the style of the courtly Kneller. Mr. Hesselius, however, had married an American lady, and was living near Annapolis. To him our young artist looked for the benefit of instruction; and taking with him as a present one of his finest saddles, requested to see him paint a picture. Thus instructed, he succeeded in painting the portraits of several of his friends, much to their gratification and pleasure to himself, but little to the advantage of his neglected saddlery.

Tempted by an offer of his brother in law, Captain Polk, he accompanied him in his schooner to Boston, where he became acquainted with Mr. Copley, who received him kindly and lent him a picture to copy. The sight of Mr. Copley's picture room afforded him great enjoyment and instruction. He returned with increased knowledge, and was patronized by Mr. Arbunkle, whose family he had painted; besides several neighbours in Virginia. On his return to Annapolis it was decided by his friends that he must go to England, and several gentlemen very liberally subscribed to raise a fund for that purpose, to be repaid by paintings on his return, which enabled him to undertake the voyage to London, furnished with letters of recommendation to Mr. West, Mr. Jennings, and others.

Mr. West received him with the greatest kindness, and freely gave him instructions in drawing and painting. From an Italian he learned to model in wax; Mr. Flaxman senior, instructed him in the art of moulding and casting plaister figures. But when he had been more than a year in London, and his diminished funds reminded him of returning to America, Mr. West earnestly persuaded him to remain another year, kindly offering him a residence in his own house. Additional remittances from America, and some portraits which he painted in London, through the recommendations of Mr. Jennings, enabled him to prolong his stay; during which he made great improvement in oil painting, learned to paint in miniature, and executed some mezzotinto engravings. At this time Stuart and Trumbull were likewise students with Mr. West.

On his return to America, he found constant employment at portrait painting, both in Annapolis and Baltimore. Here he invited his brothers St. George and James to join his family, and instructed them, as well as his sisters, in drawing and painting. To commemorate this happy groupe, he painted the large family piece which is in the Philadel-phia Museum, to which, in his old age, he added a faithful mastiff. In several visits which he had paid to Philadelphia, having found employment, he determined to settle there, which he did in the year 1776; but the increasing troubles, produced by the contest with the parent country, excited his patriotism to join in popular meetings, where he was distinguished for his ardour. He raised a company of volunteers, which elected him their captain. With them he sought the army of General Washington, and was engaged in the battles of Trenton and Germantown; his family having retired from Philadelphia into the country, enduring many privations.

In camp he painted the portraits of several distinguished officers, which was the commencement of his invaluable Gallery of American characters; and it was at the moment he was painting a miniature of General Washington at a small farm-house in New Jersey, a letter was received announcing the surrender of Cornwallis. Mr. Peale had his table and chair near the window, and Washington was sitting on the side of a bed; the room being too small for another chair. His aid-de-camp, Colonel Tilghman, was present. It was an interesting moment; but the sitting was continued, as the miniature was intended for Mrs. Washington.

Notwithstanding his fondness for the peaceful employment of the pencil, he was influenced by the spirit of the times to join in public meetings, where, being often chairman, he was drawn into notice, and appointed to offices of great responsibility. In 1779 he represented Philadelphia in the Legislative Assembly, and zealously co-operated in passing the law for the abolition of slavery. But he ever afterwards forbore meddling with politics, and scrupulously confined his attention to painting, mechanical inventions and occupations. At this time he was much employed, being, for about fifteen years, the only portrait painter in the western world.

In the year 1785, the idea of making a Museum of Natural History first occurred to him. It was suggested by some bones of the Mammoth which were brought to him to make drawings from them, and were placed in his picture gallery, which contained a valuable and increasing collection of portraits of characters distinguished in the revolutionary struggles. This new pursuit soon engrossed all his thoughts, and furnished a never-ending occupation for all his industry, ingenuity, and perseverance. Unacquainted with the European modes of proceeding, he had every thing to discover; and years elapsed before he could succeed in preserving his specimens of animals from the depredations of insects. The writer of this article has seen hundreds of birds and beasts, when better specimens were prepared, burnt in piles—a sacrifice on the altar of experience. Many citizens and strangers contributed to enlarge his collection, and, in a few years, his picture gallery, at the corner of Lombard and Third streets, after several enlargements, was found to be too small for his Museum. It was then removed to the Philosophical Hall, and there was greatly augmented, especially with the skeleton of the Mammoth,* which was discovered in Ulster county, N. York State, and disinterred at great expense and labour. Thus, a few bones of the Mammoth accidentally suggested the idea of a Museum, which, subsequently furnished its founder with the means of procuring and displaying to the world the first skeleton of that antedeluvian wonder, since classified under the name of Mastadon; which, in its turn contributed to give character and value to a Museum that now ranks on an equality with the most celebrated of Europe, founded and supported as they are, by the wealth of powerful governments.

Hitherto no person in America had presented the subject of Natural History in the attractive shape of lectures. With the view of combining the result of his own observations and discoveries, with the facts and observations that were to be found scattered in various European works, Mr. Peale delivered at the Museum a course of lectures at once popular and scientific, which were attended by the most

* In the spring of 1801, receiving information from a scientific correspondent in the State of New York, that in the autumn of 1799 many bones of the Mammoth had been found in digging a marle-pit in the vicinity of Newburgh, which is situated on the river Hudson, sixty-seven miles from the city of New York, my father, Charles Willson Peale, immediately proceeded to the spot, and through the politeness of Dr. Graham, whose residence on the banks of the Wall-kill enabled him to be present when most of the bones were dug up, received every information with respect to what had been done, and the most probable means of future success. The bones that had been found were then in the possession of the farmer who discovered them, heaped on the floor of his garret or granary, where they were occasionally visited by the curious. These my father was fortunate to make a purchase of, together with the right of digging for the remainder, and, immediately packing them up, sent them on to Philadelphia. They consisted of all the neck, most of the vertebræ of the back, and some of the tail; most of the ribs, in greater part broken; both scapulæ; both humeri, with the radii and ulnæ; one femur; a tibia of one leg, and a fibula of the other; some large fragments of the head; many of the fore and hind feet bones; the pelvis, somewhat broken; and a large fragment, five feet long, of one tusk, about mid-way. He therefore was in want of some of the back and tail bones, some of the ribs, the under jaw, one whole tusk and part of the other, the breast bone, one thigh, and a tibia and fibula, and many of the feet bones. But as the farmer's fields were then in grain, the enterprise of further investigation was postponed for a short time.

The whole of this part of the country abounding with morasses, solid enough for cattle to walk over, containing peat, or turf, and shell-marle, it is the custom of the farmers to assist each other, in order to acquire a quantity of the marle for manure. Pits are dug generally twelve feet long and five feet wide at the top, lessening to three feet at the bottom. The peat or turf is thrown on lands not immediately in use; and the marle, after mellowing through the winter, is in the spring scattered over the cultivated fields—the most luxuriant crops are the consequence. It was in digging one of these, on the farm of John Masten, that one of the men, thrusting his spade deeper than usual, struck what he supposed to be a log of wood, but on cutting it to ascertain the kind, to his astonishment, he found it was a bone: it was quickly cleared from the surrounding earth, and proved to be that of the thigh, three feet nine inches in length, and eighteen inches in circumference, in the smallest part. The search was continued, and the same evening several other bones were discovered. The fame of it soon spread through the neighbourhood, and excited a general interest in the pursuit: all were eager, at the expense of some exertions, to gratify their curiosity in seeing the ruins of an animal so gigantic, of whose bones very few among them had ever heard, and over which they had so often unconsciously trod. For the two succeeding days upwards of an hundred men were actively engaged, encouraged by several gentlemen, chiefly physicians of the neighbourhood, and success the most sanguine attended their labours: but, unfortunately, the habits of the men requiring the use of spirits, it was afforded them in too

great profusion, and they quickly became so impatient and unruly that they had nearly destroyed the skeleton; and, in one or two instances, using oxen and chains to drag them from the clay and marle, the head, hips, and tusks were much broken; some parts being drawn out, and others left behind. So great a quantity of water, from copious springs, bursting from the bottom, rose upon the men, that it required several score of hands to lade it out, with all the milk-pails, buckets, and bowls, they could collect in the neighbourhood. All their ingenuity was exerted to conquer difficulties that every hour increased upon their hands; they even made and sunk a large coffer-dam, and within it found many valuable small bones. The fourth day so much water had risen in the pit, that they had not courage to attack it again. In this state we found it in 1801.

It was a curious circumstance attending the purchase of these bones, that the sum which was paid for them was little more than one-third of what had been offered to the farmer for them by another, and refused, not long before. This anecdote may not be uninteresting to the moralist, and I shall explain it. The farmer of German extraction—and like many others in America, speaking the language of his fathers better than that of his country—was born on his farm; he was brought up to it as a business, and it continued to be his pleasure in old age; not because it was likely to free him from labour, but because profit, and the prospect of profit, cheered him in it, until the end was forgotten in the means. Intent upon manuring his lands to increase its production, (always laudable), he felt no interest in the fossil-shells contained in his morass; and had it not been for the men who dug with him, and those whose casual attention was arrested, or who were drawn by report to the spot, for him the bones might have rotted in the hole in which he discovered them; this he confessed to me would have been his conduct, certain that after the surprise of the moment they were good for nothing but to rot as manure. But the learned physician, the reverend divine, to whom he had been accustomed to look upwards, gave importance to the objects which excited the vulgar stare of his more inquisitive neighbours: he therefore joined his exertions to theirs, to recover as many of the bones as possible. With him, hope was every thing; with the men curiosity did much, but rum did more, and some little was owing to certain prospects which they had of sharing in the future possible profit. It is possible he might have encouraged this idea; his fear of it, however, seems to have given him some uneasiness; for when he was offered a small sum for the bones, it appeared too little to divide; and when a larger sum, he fain would have engrossed the whole of it, or persuade himself that the real value might be something greater. Ignorant of what had been offered him, my father's application was in a critical moment, and the farmer accepted his price, on condition that he should receive a new gun for his son, and new gowns for his wife and daughters, with some other articles of the same class. The farmer was glad they were out of his granary, and that they were in a few days to be two hundred miles distant; and my father was no less pleased with the consciousness, and on which every one complimented him, that they were in the hands of one who would spare no exertions to make the best use of them. The neighbours,

distinguished citizens, of both sexes, who enjoyed the opportunity of seeing the objects which they heard explained.

But it was not sufficient that he had written these lectures; they must be delivered by himself; a task, the difficulty of which was increased by the recent loss of some of his front teeth. His ingenuity was soon at work to supply this deficiency, and with remarkable perseverance he succeeded, first in ivory, and finally in making complete sets

who had assisted the farmer in this discovery, envious of his good fortune, sued him for a share in the profit; but they gained nothing more than a dividend of the costs; it appearing that they had been satisfied with the gratification of their curiosity, and the quality and quantity of the rum; no one could prove that he had given them reason to hope for a share in the price of any thing his land might happen to produce.

Not willing to lose the advantage of an uncommonly dry season, when the springs in the morass were low, we proceeded on the arduous enterprise. In New York every article was provided which might be necessary in surmounting expected difficulties; such as a pump, ropes, pullies, augers, &c.; boards and plank were provided in the neighbourhood, and timber was in sufficient plenty on the spot.

Confident that nothing could be done without having a perfect command of the water, the first idea was to drain it by a ditch; but the necessary distance of perhaps half a mile, presented a length of labour that appeared immense. It was therefore resolved to throw the water into a natural basin, about sixty feet distant, the upper edge of which was about ten feet above the level of the water. An ingenious millwright constructed the machinery, and, after a week of close labour, completed a large scaffolding and a wheel twenty feet diameter, wide enough for three or four men to walk a-breast in: a rope round this turned a small spindle, which worked a chain of buckets regulated by a floating cylinder; the water thus raised, was emptied into a trough, which conveyed it to the basin; a ship's pump assisted, and, towards the latter part of the operation, a pair of half barrels, in removing the mud. This machine worked so powerfully, that in the second day the water was lowered so much as to enable them to dig; and in a few hours they were rewarded with several small bones.

The road which passed through this farm was a highway, and the attention of every traveller was arrested by the coaches, wagons, chaises, and horses, which animated the road, or were collected at the entrance of the field: rich and poor, men, women, and children, all flocked to see the operation; and a swamp always noted as the solitary abode of snakes and frogs, became the active scene of curiosity and bustle: most of the spectators were astonished at the purpose which could prompt such vigorous and expensive exertions, in a manner so unprecedented, and so foreign to the pursuits for which they were noted. But the amusement was not wholly on their side; and the variety of company not only amused us, but tended to encourage the workmen, each of whom, before so many spectators, was ambitious of signalizing himself by the number of his discoveries.

For several weeks no exertions were spared, and the most unremitting were required to insure success; bank after bank fell in; the increase of water was a constant impediment, the extreme coldness of which benumbed the workmen. Each day required some new expedient, and the carpenter was always making additions to the machinery; every day bones and pieces of bones were found between six and seven feet deep, but none of the most important ones. But the greatest obstacle to the search was occasioned by the shell marle which formed the lower stratum; this rendered thin by the springs at the bottom, was, by the weight of the whole morass, always pressed upwards on the workmen to a certain height, which, without an incalculable expense, it was impossible to prevent. Twenty-five hands at high wages were almost constantly employed at work which was so uncomfortable and severe, that nothing but their anxiety to see the head, and particularly the under jaw, could have kept up their resolution. The patience of employer and workmen was at length exhausted, and the work relinquished without obtaining those interesting parts, the want of which rendered it impossible to form a complete skeleton.

It would not have been a very difficult matter to put these bones together,

and they would have presented the general appearance of the skeleton; but the under jaw was broken to pieces in the first attempt to get out the bones, and nothing but the teeth and a few fragments of it were now found; the tail was mostly wanting, and some toe-bones. It was, therefore, a desirable object to obtain some knowledge of these deficient parts, but if possible to find some other skeleton in such order as to see the position, and correctly to ascertain the number of the bones. In the course of eighteen years there had been found within twelve miles of this spot, a bone or two in several different places; concerning these we have made particular inquiries, but found that most of the morasses had been since drained, and consequently either the bones had been exposed to a certain decay; or else so deep, that a fortune might have been spent in the fruitless pursuit. But through the polite attention of *Dr. Galatan*, we were induced to examine a small morass, eleven miles distant from the former, belonging to Capt. J. Barber, where, eight years before, four ribs had been found in digging a pit. From the description which was given of their position, and the appearance of the morass, we began our operations with all the vigour a certainty of success could inspire. Nearly a week was consumed in making a ditch, by which all the water was carried off, except what a hand-pump could occasionally empty: the digging, therefore, was less difficult than that at Masten's, though still tedious and unpleasant; particularly as the sun, unclouded as it had been for seven weeks, poured its scorching rays on the morass, so circumscribed by trees, that the western breeze afforded no refreshment; yet nothing could exceed the ardour of the men, particularly of one, a gigantic and athletic negro, who exulted in choosing the most laborious tasks, although he seemed melting with heat. Almost an entire set of ribs were found, lying nearly together, and very entire; but as none of the back bones were found near them (a sufficient proof of their having been scattered) our latitude for search was extended to very uncertain limits; therefore, after working about two weeks, and finding nothing belonging to the head but two rotten tusks, (part of one of them is with the skeleton here) three or four small grinders, a few vertebræ of the back and tail, a broken scapula, some toe-bones, and the ribs, found between four and seven feet deep—a reluctant terminating pause ensued.

These bones were kept distinct from those found at Masten's, as it would not be proper to incorporate into one skeleton any other than the bones belonging to it; and nothing more was intended than collate the corresponding parts. These bones were chiefly valuable as specimens of the individual parts; but no bones were found among them which were deficient in the former collection, and therefore our chief object was defeated. To have failed in so small a morass was rather discouraging to the idea of making another attempt; and yet the smallness of the morass was, perhaps, the cause of our failure, as it was extremely probable the bones we could not find were long since decayed, from being situated on the rising slope at no considerable depth, unprotected by the shell-marle, which lay only in the lower part of the basin forming the morass. When every exertion was given over, we could not but look at the surrounding unexplored parts with some concern, uncertain how near we might have been to the discovery of all that we wanted, and regretting the probability that, in consequence of the drain we had made, a few years would wholly destroy the venerable objects of our research.

Almost in despair at our failure in the last place, where so much was expected, it was with very little spirit we mounted our horses, on another inquiry. Crossing the Wall-kill at the falls, we ascended over a double swelling hill into a rudely cultivated country, about twenty miles west from the Hudson, where, in a thinly settled neighbourhood, lived the honest farmer Peter Millspaw, who, three years before, had discovered several bones: from his log-hut he accompanied us to the morass. It was impossible to resist the

of porcelain teeth, not only for himself, but for his friends and others, at a time when no other person in the United States had succeeded in the attempt.

About the period when the Museum was commenced, Loutherbourg in London had got up an exhibition of transparent paintings with moveable effects. A description of these excited an irresistible desire to effect the same purposes. Here was a vast field opened for his taste and invention; for his labour day and night, and his morning dreams. At length, the public in crowds witnessed, at the end of his long gallery of portraits, these magic pictures. A perspective view of Market street, gradually darkening into the gloom of night. The street lamps are successively lighted and sparkle in the diminishing perspective; the clouds disperse and the pale moon rises. Another picture represented a prospect in the country, dimly seen at night;

—the cock crows, the horizon brightens gradually into the glow of sunrise, gay with the chirping of birds which fly from tree to tree;—presently the clouds arise, thick and dark, till brightened on their varying edges by the lightning's flash, accompanied by the roll of thunder;—the rain begins to fall, increasing to a heavy shower; but it clears away and exhibits a splendid rainbow which commences and dies away gradually. Other pieces admirably represented the battle between the Bon Homme Richard, commanded by Paul Jones and the British frigate Serapis; and the gorgeous display of the temple of Pandemonium.

Many years before this, an attempt was made to found an Academy of the Fine Arts by the few artists who found occupation in Philadelphia, chiefly engravers, with Mr. Rush the carver, and some foreign artists then sojourning with us. Landscape and miniature painters, and with them the

solemnity of the approach to this venerable spot, which was surrounded by a fence of safety to the cattle without. Here we fastened our horses, and followed our guide into the centre of the morass, or rather marshy forest, where every step was taken on rotten timber and the spreading roots of tall trees, the luxuriant growth of a few years, half of which were tottering over our heads. Breathless silence had here taken her reign amid unhealthy fogs, and nothing was heard but the fearful crash of some mouldering branch or towering beach. It was almost a dead level, and the holes dug for the purpose of obtaining manure, out of which a few bones had been taken six or seven years before, were full of water, and connected with others containing a vast quantity; so that to empty one was to empty them all; yet a last effort might be crowned with success; and, since so many difficulties *had been* conquered, it was resolved to embrace the only opportunity that now offered for any farther discovery. Machinery was accordingly erected, pumps and buckets were employed, and a long course of troughs conducted the water among the distant roots to a fall of a few inches, by which the men were enabled, unmolested, unless by the caving in of the banks, to dig on every side from the spot where the first discovery of the bones had been made.

Here alternate success and disappointment amused and fatigued us for a long while; until, with empty pockets, low spirits, and languid workmen, we were about to quit the morass with but a small collection, though in good preservation, of ribs, toe, and leg bones, &c. In the meanwhile, to leave no means untried, the ground was searched in various directions with long-pointed rods and cross-handles: after some practice we were able to distinguish by feeling, whatever substances we touched harder than the soil; and by this means, in a very unexpected direction, though not more than twenty feet from the first bones that were discovered, struck upon a large collection of bones which were dug to and taken up, with every possible care. They proved to be a humerus, or large bone of the right leg, with the radius and ulna of the left, the right scapula, the atlas, several toe-bones, and the great object of our pursuit, a complete UNDER JAW!

After such a variety of labour and length of fruitless expectation, this success was extremely grateful to all parties, and the unconscious woods echoed with the repeated huzzas, which could not have been more animated if every tree had participated in the joy. "Gracious God, what a jaw! how many animals have been crushed by it!" was the exclamation of all; a fresh supply of grog went around, and the hearty fellows, covered with mud, continued the search with increasing vigour. The upper part of the head was found twelve feet distant, but so extremely rotten that we could only preserve the teeth and a few fragments. In its form it exactly resembled the head found at Masten's; but, as that was much injured by rough usage, this, from its small depth beneath the surface, had the cranium so rotted

away as only to show the form around the teeth, and thence extending to the condyles of the neck; the rotten bone formed a black and greasy mould above that part which was still entire, yet so tender as to break to pieces on lifting it from its bed.

This collection was rendered still more complete by the addition of those formerly taken up, and presented to us by Drs. Graham and Post. They were a rib, the sternum, a femur, tibia and fibula, and a patella or knee-pan. One of the ribs had found its way into an obscure farmhouse, ten miles distant, to which we fortunately traced it.

Thus terminated this strange and laborious campaign of three months, during which we were wonderfully favoured, although vegetation suffered, by the driest season which had occurred within eight years. Our venerable relics were carefully packed up in distinct cases; and, loading two wagons with them, we bade adieu to the vallies and stupendous mountains of Shawangunk: so called by their former inhabitants, the Indians of the Lenape tribe. The three sets of bones were kept distinct: with the two collections which were most numerous it was intended to form two skeletons, by still keeping them separate, and filling up the deficiencies in each by artificial imitations from the other, and from counterparts in themselves. For instance, in order to complete the first skeleton, which was found at Masten's, the under jaw was to be modelled from this, which is the only entire one that has yet been discovered, although we have seen considerable fragments of at least ten different jaws; while, on the other hand, in the skeleton just discovered at Barber's, the upper jaw, which was found in the extreme of decay, was to be completed, so far as it goes, from the more solid fragment of the head belonging to the skeleton found at Masten's. Several feet-bones in this skeleton were to be made from that; and a few in that were to be made from this. In this the right humerus being real, the imitation for the left one could be made with the utmost certainty; and the radius and ulna of the left leg being real, those on the right side would follow, of course, &c. The collection of ribs in both cases was almost entire; therefore, having discovered from a correspondence between the number of vertebræ and ribs in both animals, that there were nineteen pair of the latter, it was necessary in only four or five instances to supply the counterparts, by correct models from the real bones. In this manner the two skeletons were formed, and are in both instances composed of the appropriate bones of the animal, or exact imitations from the real bones in the same skeleton, or from those of the same proportion in the other. Nothing in either skeleton is imaginary; and what we have not unquestionable authority for, we leave deficient; which happens in only two instances, the *summit* of the head, and the *end* of the tail.—*Godman's Nat. Hist. by Rembrandt Peale.*

7

Italian Sculptor Ceracchi (who afterwards conspired against the life of Buonaparte). Among these Mr. Peale was the only portrait painter in oil. At his house the meetings were held, and the conversations were often interesting under all the excitements of imagination and genius; but they ended in a separation into two unproductive parties; the native artists contented with a school of art, and the foreigners swelling with a mighty scheme of a national Academy.

In the year 1794 another experiment was made at Mr. Peale's—an academy was formed; some plaister casts were collected, and arrangements were made to draw from the life. When the person (a baker) who was engaged to stand as the model, found himself surrounded by new faces and penetrating eyes, he shrunk from the scrutiny, and precipitately fled. In this dilemma Mr. Peale stripped and presented himself as the model to his fellow artists. An exhibition was likewise got up, intended to be annual. It was opened in the Hall of Independence; comprised a very respectable display of pictures, chiefly lent by private gentlemen, and was well attended by the public.

It was not until 1810 that a foundation could be laid for a permanent Academy. Again the amateurs of the Arts were invited to meet at Mr. Peale's; but their number was so small, and their influence over the public mind so limited, that nothing but the most zealous exertions of Mr. Joseph Hopkinson could have availed in procuring the funds which were necessary to erect a suitable building, and to import from Europe the requisite plaister casts. Mr. Peale and his son, who was recently from Europe, laboured incessantly to mend and display these objects, and to organize the drawing academies. He lived to see and contribute to seventeen annual exhibitions.

Early rising, temperate repasts, and industrious habits, had invigorated his constitution, and he had reached his eighty-fifth year with but little interruption 'to his health, and pleasantly talked of living to be at least a hundred years old. The manner of his death was strictly accordant with the peculiarities of his life; for it was not so much the consequence of old age as of too much youth, in imprudently carrying his own trunk to get up with a stage which he feared would leave him behind. This induced a violent palpitation and disorder of his heart, from which he had scarcely recovered, when he indiscreetly mounted the highest ladder at the new building of the Arcade, the upper rooms of which were being constructed to hold his Museum. This brought on a relapse and his speedy and lamented death, in 1827; leaving his Museum as a joint stock to his children; Raphael, Angelica Kaufman, Rembrandt, Rubens, Sophonisba Carriera, Linnæus, Franklin, Sybilla, Meriam, Elizabeth, and Titian.

Few men have passed through a greater variety of scenes and occupations. Perhaps in the organization of his mind there was too great a propensity to indulge in every novel occupation; certainly there was a peculiarity of fancy which controlled him in these enjoyments; he loved to do what nobody around him could do, and exhibited the most extraordinary industry, perseverance, and ingenuity to accomplish his purposes. His chief delight, though of a cheerful and social temper, was to find himself alone in the trackless ocean of experiments, contending with the rough elements and surmounting difficulties as they followed in successive waves never sinking, never despairing. At first a saddler, harness and coach maker; then a silversmith and watchmaker; it was not till his 26th year that his eyes opened to the boundless fields of art; but in this pursuit he mingled the greatest variety, painting in oil, in crayons, and in miniature; modelling in clay, wax and plaister; sawing his own ivory, moulding his glasses, and making the shagreen cases for the miniatures which he painted, at a time when none of these articles could be procured, owing to the derangements of a revolutionary war. He made himself a wooden mannequin or lay-figure, upon which to cast his draperies; made a violin and guitar, and assisted in the construction of the first organ built in Philadelphia. But it was chiefly in multitudinous operations connected with his Museum that he found continual employment for his invention and mechanical propensities. Transparent paintings with changeable effects of light and colour, and figures in motion; the preservation of every variety of animals; the moulding of glass eyes, carving wooden limbs, upon which to stretch the skins of his quadrupeds, with anatomical accuracy, &c. Many precious months of his life were consumed in perfecting, with Mr. J. H. Hawkins, their Polygraph, which became one of his untiring hobbies, as he never wrote a letter afterwards without preserving a cotemporaneous duplicate.

For a number of years he supplied the dificiencies of his teeth with ivory of his own manufacture, and finally succeeded in making them of porcelain, not only for himself and family, but for others, as he prided himself on being the only operator in this style in America.

We shall close this sketch by an observation of Colonel Trumbull: "That an interesting comparison might be drawn between Mr. Peale and his countryman Mr. West, who was a striking instance how much could be accomplished with moderate genius, by a steady and undeviating course directed to a single object; to become the first Historical painter of his age; whilst the other, with a more lively genius, was able to acquire an extraordinary excellence in many arts, between which his attention was too much divided. For had he confined his operations to one pursuit he probably would have attained the highest excellence in the Fine Arts."

However praiseworthy may have been his industry; remarkable or amusing his ingenuity; and productive his perseverance to the success of his Museum—he possessed a higher claim to the remembrance and esteem of his countrymen. He was a mild, benevolent, good man.

COMMON DEER (BUCK, DOE AND FAWN)

COMMON DEER.
CERVUS VIRGINIANUS.

Cervus Virginianus. Gmelin.—*Fallow Deer.* Catesby, *App.* ii. 28. Lawson, *Carol.* 123.—*Virginian Deer.* Pennant, *Arct. Zool.* i. 32.—*Caricon femelle.* Buffon, 12. *pl.* 44.—*Cerf de la Louisiane.* G. Cuv. *Ossmen. Foss.* iv. 34. Regn. *animal.* i. 263.—*Cerf de Virginie.* Desm. *Mammal. sp.* 679. *p.* 442.—*Common Deer.* Godman, i. 306.—Philadelphia *Museum.*

The word Deer is derived either from the Teutonic *deor*, or from the Greek Θηϛ, and is very variously written and pronounced, not only by different nations, but also in different ages. These well known quadrupeds belong to the great order of Pecora or Ruminants; an order, as is observed by Cuvier, exceedingly natural and well determined, nearly all the animals composing it, being formed on the same model, the Camel alone presenting some slight exceptions to the common character of the group.

The genus Deer, consists of such animals of this order as are furnished with deciduous horns or antlers, destitute of a horny sheath. They are generally remarkable not only for the elegance of their form, the symmetry of their proportions and swiftness of their motions, but also for the excellence of their flesh. Hence it is not surprising that they have been eagerly hunted in every age, as well for subsistence as for amusement. The most striking and curious parts of their conformation are the horns, or those osseous productions of the forehead which are detached and reproduced annually, and which, except in the Rein Deer, are exclusively appropriated to the males. This annual shedding of the horns, however, is not peculiar to the whole genus, but appears to be restricted to such species as reside in cold or temperate climates, or in whom these appendages are of a large size. This provision of nature is a most inexplicable phenomenon as regards its utility, and yet the mode in which the process is effected is subordinate to fixed and immutable laws.

The word horn, which is generally applied to the antlers of the Deer kind, is apt to lead to erroneous ideas on the subject, as this antler is a real bone, formed in the same manner, and constituted of the same integral parts as other bones. These protuberances begin to be developed at a given age; the first appearance being a tubercle, which, in most cases, gradually rises into a simple antler, though in some species it branches off into ramifications; after a cer-

tain period the development is arrested, and finally the horn is detached and falls off.

The form and disposition of the antlers differ in every species, and the flattened or palmated shape of them in some, seems to be a provision of nature to enable the animals to obtain their food from beneath the snow, for it is a remarkable fact that this structure is almost wholly confined to such as inhabit high latitudes, and is developed in proportion to the length and severity of the climate.

The sense of smell is very delicate in these animals, and they are exceedingly select in their choice of food, applying to it the nostrils, and sometimes the spiracula, which seem to communicate, in some manner, with the olfactory apparatus. This spiraculum or sinus is not found in all species, some having only a fold of the skin or none, whilst in others it forms a sack. The French call them *larmiers*, believing that they are receptacles for tears; this idea has also been adopted by poets: thus, Shakspeare gives the following touching description of a wounded stag:

> " The wretched animal heav'd forth such groans,
> That their discharge did stretch his leathern coat
> Almost to bursting; and the big round tears
> Coursed one another down his innocent nose
> In piteous chase."

The voice of the genus is in general disagreeable. The females produce one or two fawns at a time. In temperate regions this takes place in the spring. The intellectual character of the Deer is far from contemptible; rendering the chase of the stag very curious. The amusement of hunting has been as assiduously cultivated among civilized nations as with the savage tribes who depend upon it for their subsistence. In fact, it was considered as an art, and accommodated with a set of technical phrases. Thus, in the old works on "Venerie," we find that the young animal in the first six months of its life was called a *calf* or *hind calf*, it then became a *knobber;* then a *pricket, brock,* or *staggard;* next a *stag,* and after that a *hart:* the female, from a *hind calf,* becomes first a *hearse* and then a *hind.* The stag is said to *harbour* in the place in which he resides; when he cries he is said to *bell;* the print of his hoof is the *slot;* the tail the *single,* his excrement the *feumet;* his horns are termed his *head,* and are, in the first year, *broches;* in the third year, *spears;* in the fourth year, the part bearing the antlers is called the *beam;* he has also *antlers, sur-antlers,* and *royal-antlers.* These animals afford various articles of utility to man. The firm and solid texture of the horns fits them for handles to knives and other domestic utensils. The skin is dressed into excellent leather. The flesh, as we have before observed, affords a pleasant and wholesome food.

RED FOX

RED FOX.

CANIS (VULPES) FULVUS.

Renard de Virginie. Palisot de Beauvois. *Bul. soc. Phil.*—*Large Red Fox of the Plains.* Lewis & Clark.—*Red Fox.* Sabine. *App. to Franklin's Journey,* 656. Godman, vol. i. 276.—*American Fox.* Richardson, *Faun. am. bor.* 91.—*Canis fulvus,* Desm. *Mamm.* 203. Icon F. Cuv. *Mam. Lithog.*— J. Doughty's *Collection.*

The various species of the Fox have been classed by most naturalists in the genus *Canis* Lin. together with the wolf and jackal. From these animals, however, they differ in many important particulars. In the dogs, the pupil of the eye is circular and diurnal; whilst in the Fox, it is linear and nocturnal. The tail is also more bushy, the nose more pointed, and the scent stronger than in the former. There is likewise a very marked dissimilarity in many of their habits and manners; thus the Fox burrows, which the dog does not, the voice of the former is rather a yelp than a bark, &c.

Most of the species of the Fox have the same cunning and sagacity, the same eagerness after prey, and commit the same ravages among game, birds, poultry, and the lesser quadrupeds. They are exceedingly fond of honey, and will attack hives and the nests of the wild bee, for the sake of the spoil; in these exploits they frequently meet with so rough a reception, as to force them to retire, that they may roll on the ground and thus crush their numerous and vindictive assailants; but the moment they have effected this, they return to the charge and are generally successful. Foxes will also eat any sort of insect, fruit, &c. and are very destructive in vineyards. This latter propensity was observed at a very early period. "Take us the Foxes, the little Foxes that spoil the vines, for our vines have tender grapes."*

Foxes are very fond of basking in the sun; in fact their general time of rest is in the day time, during which period they appear listless and inactive, without they are excited by fear or some other stimulus. They sleep in a round form like the dog, and also resemble that animal in the ease with which they are awakened, it being almost impossible to come on them unawares, for even when they are in an apparently sound sleep, the slightest noise, made near them, will arouse them. The moment night sets in, all their faculties are awakened; they then begin their gambols and depredations, continuing in rapid and almost unceasing motion till day break. Most, if not all, the species live in burrows; these are generally composed of

* Solomon's Song, ii. 15.

several chambers, and are provided with more than one entrance, by which they may make their escape in cases of extremity. One of the great characteristics of the Fox, is their extreme prudence and almost matchless cunning, which are exemplified not only in their stratagems to obtain prey, but also in their numerous wiles in order to avoid their pursuers. Dr. Richardson states, that the arctic Fox appears to have the power of decoying other animals within his reach, by imitating their voices: this is confirmed by Captain Lyon, who states, "that while tenting, we observed a Fox prowling on a hill side, and heard him for several hours afterwards in different places, imitating the cry of a brent goose." Crantz, in his History of Greenland, informs us, that this species also exert an extraordinary degree of cunning in their mode of obtaining fish. They go into the water, and make a splash with their feet in order to excite their curiosity, and when they come up, seize them. The mode in which some species entrap

This character of cunning and extreme prudence in the Fox, renders him extremely difficult to be destroyed, or taken. As soon as he has acquired a little experience, he is not to be deceived by the snares laid for him, and the moment he recognizes them, nothing can induce him to approach them, even when suffering the severest pangs of hunger. The scent which the Fox leaves behind him being exceeding strong, he appears sensible of that circumstance, and uses every artifice to bewilder his pursuers and throw them out of their track. He generally takes advantage of the wind, and often crosses rivers, swims down small streams or runs along the top of a wall, in order to interrupt the continuity of the scent, and puzzle the dogs. This timid and prudential character, however, completely disappears in the female when she has young ones to nurse and defend. Maternal instinct, which is forcibly felt by all species of animals, and effaces for a time their natural propensities, is peculiarly striking in the Fox. There is no sentiment so universal in its nature and so wholly disinterested as this; none in which personal danger is so completely unheeded and disregarded. A mother never hesitates an instant in facing the most appalling danger, or enduring the utmost privations, risking every thing, even life itself, for the preservation of her infant offspring. She that at other times was timid and gentle, now becomes bold, fierce, and resolute; unshaken by all that is trying, undeterred by all that is menacing. Thus the female Fox watches with unceasing care over her young, assiduously providing for all their wants, and exhibiting a fearlessness wholly different from her usual disposition.

13

RUFFED GROUSE OR PHEASANT

RUFFED GROUS, OR PHEASANT.

TETRAO UMBELLUS.

Arct. Zool. p. 301, *No.* 179.—*Ruffed Heath-cock, or Grous,* Edw. 248.—*La Gelinote hupèe de Pennsylvanie,* Briss. i. 214.—*Pl. Enl.* 104.—Buff. ii. 281.—*Phil. Trans.* 82, 393.—Turt. *Syst.* 454.

The manners of the Pheasant are solitary; they are seldom found in coveys of more than four or five together, and more usually in pairs or singly. They leave their sequestered haunts in the woods early in the morning, and seek the path or road to pick up gravel, and glean among the droppings of the horses. In travelling among the mountains that bound the Susquehanna, I was always able to furnish myself with an abundant supply of these birds, every morning, without leaving the path. If the weather be foggy, or lowering, they are sure to be seen in such situations. They generally move along with great stateliness, spreading their long tails in a fan-like manner. The drumming, as it is usually called, of the Pheasant, is another singularity of this species. This is performed by the male alone. In walking through solitary woods frequented by these birds, a stranger is surprised by suddenly hearing a kind of thumping, very similar to that produced by striking two full-blown ox-bladders together, but much louder; the strokes, at first, are slow and distinct; but gradully increase in rapidity until they run into each other, resembling the rumbling sound of very distant thunder, dying away gradually on the ear. After a few minutes pause, this is again repeated; and in a calm day may be heard nearly half a mile off. This drumming is most common in spring, and is the call of the cock to his favourite female. In the early part of the season, it frequently happens that this drumming attracts the attention of some rival cock, which is led to the spot from whence it proceeds, when a most furious battle takes place between them as competitors for the hen, and owing to the gameness of these birds, it lasts for a considerable time; victory, however, is generally on the side of the injured party, owing probably to the greater degree of fierceness with which he combats, in protection of his favourite, than that exhibited by his antagonist. They fight keenly, and strike exceeding hard with their wings, alternately seizing each other with their bills. This drumming is produced in the following manner. —(*Vide Plate*) The bird, standing on the old prostrate log, generally in a retired and sheltered situation, lowers his wings, erects his expanded tail, contracts his throat, elevates the two tufts of feathers on the neck, and inflates his whole body, something in the manner of the turkey cock, strutting and wheeling about with great stateliness. After a few manœuvres of this kind, he begins to strike with his stiffened wings in short and quick strokes, which become more and more rapid until they run into each other, as has been already described. This is most common in the morning and evening, though I have heard them drumming at all hours of the day. By means of this, the gunner is led to the place of his retreat; though to those unacquainted with the sound, there is great deception in the supposed distance, it generally appearing to be much nearer than it really is.

The Pheasant begins to pair in April, and builds its nest early in May. This is placed on the ground at the root of a bush, old log, or other sheltered and solitary situation, well surrounded with withered leaves. Unlike that of the Quail, it is open above, and is usually composed of dry leaves and grass. The eggs are from nine to fifteen in number, of a brownish white, without any spots, and nearly as large as those of a pullet. The young leave the nest as soon as hatched, and are directed by the cluck of the mother, very much in the manner of the common hen. On being surprised, she exhibits all the distress and affectionate manœuvres of the Quail, and of most other birds, to lead you away from the spot. I once started a hen Pheasant, with a single young one, seemingly only a few days old; there might have been more, but I observed only this one. The mother fluttered before me for a moment, but suddenly darting towards the young one, seized it in her bill, and flew off along the surface through the woods, with great steadiness and rapidity, till she was beyond my sight, leaving me in great surprise at the incident. I made a very close and active search around the spot for the rest, but without success. Here was a striking instance of something more than what is termed blind instinct, in this remarkable deviation from her usual manœuvres, when she has a numerous brood. It would have been impossible for me to injure this affectionate mother, who had exhibited such an example of presence of mind, reason, and sound judgment, as must have convinced the most bigotted advocates of mere *instinct*. To carry off a whole brood in this manner, at once, would have been impossible, and to attempt to save one at the expense of the rest, would be unnatural. She therefore usually takes the only possible mode of saving them in that case, by decoying the person in pursuit of herself, by such a natural imitation of lameness as to impose on most people. But here, in the case of a single solitary young one, she instantly altered her plan, and adopted the most simple and effectual mean for its preservation.

16

QUAIL, OR PARTRIDGE.
PERDIX VIRGINIANUS.

[Male and Female.]

Arct. Zool. 318, *No.* 185.—Catesb. *App. p.* 12.—*Virginian Quail,* Turt. *Syst. p.* 460.—*Maryland Q. Ibid.*—*Le Perdrix d'Amerique,* Briss. i. 231.—Buff. ii. 447.—*Tetrao Virginianus,* Linn. *Syst. ed.* 10, *p.* 161. *T. Marilandicus, id. ib.*—*Perdix Virginiana,* Lath, *Ind. Orn. p.* 650. *P. Marilanda, id. p.* 651.—*Caille de la Louisiane,* Buff. *Pl. Enl.* 149.—J. Doughty's *Collection.*

The Quail begins to build early in May. The nest is made on the ground, usually at the bottom of a thick tuft of grass that shelters and conceals it. The materials are leaves and fine dry grass, in considerable quantity. It is well covered above, and an opening left on one side for entrance. The female lays from fifteen to twenty-four eggs, of a pure white without any spots; and during the period of incubation are remarkably tenacious of their nest, for rather than forsake it, they will frequently sacrifice their lives, and it is by no means an uncommon occurrence for them to fall victims to the scythe. The time of incubation has been stated to me by various persons at four weeks, when the eggs were placed under the domestic hen. The young leave the nest as soon as they are freed from the shell, and are conducted about in search of food by the female; are guided by her voice, which at that time resembles the twittering of young chickens, and sheltered by her wings, in the same manner as those of the domestic fowl; but with all that secrecy and precaution for their safety, which their helplessness and greater danger require. In this situation, should the little timid family be unexpectedly surprised, the utmost alarm and consternation instantly prevail. Sometimes, when an enemy approaches, (especially the sportsman's dog,) the mother will instantly squat herself, and collect her little brood under her wings for protection, and at this time she will remain so perfectly tranquil as to permit the hand almost to grasp her, before she will attempt to escape; she will then throw herself in the path, fluttering along, and beating the ground with her wings, as if sorely wounded, using every artifice she is master of, to entice the passenger in pursuit of herself, uttering at the same time certain peculiar notes of alarm, well understood by the young, who dive separately amongst the grass, and secrete themselves till the danger is over; and the parent, having decoyed the pursuer to a safe distance, returns, by a circuitous route, to collect and lead them off. This well known manœuvre, which nine times in ten is successful, is honourable to the feelings and judgment of the bird, but a severe satire on man. The affectionate mother, as if sensible of the avaricious cruelty of his nature, tempts him with a larger prize, to save her more helpless offspring; and pays him, as avarice and cruelty ought always to be paid, with mortification and disappointment.

About the beginning of September, the Quails being now nearly full grown, and associated in flocks, or coveys, of from four or five to thirty, afford considerable sport to the gunner. And, perhaps, of all the feathered tribe which inhabit this country, none are persecuted with so much untiring vigor, as this interesting little bird; the delicacy of its flesh, its domestic qualities, and source of profit, seems to mark it for that destruction which continually awaits it.

Ranking high in our scale of game, and being universally found in this country, the Partridge, by its familiar habits, invites the sportsman, who pursues it as a source of pleasurable recreation, superior to all others; and thus, between man, hawks, and vermin, is a continual war waged against this harmless bird, and every succeeding year adds to the number and avidity of its enemies, but so great is the fecundity of the Partridge, that instead of decreasing in quantity, they appear to thrive, and multiply, in despite of the system of extermination carried on against them. The most are killed by man, and he may be fairly considered their greatest enemy; but, the Partridge is more fearful of the hawk, for when pursued by this destructive bird, terror overcomes its instinct, and it will oftimes fly, unmindful of the consequences, against a tree or house with so much force, as to be killed; in fact, frequently their whole muscular powers become so paralized by dread, that it will suffer itself to be trodden upon, or taken, without making an effort to escape.

At this time, the notes of the male are most frequent, clear, and loud. His common or early call, consists of two notes, with sometimes an introductory one, and is similar to the sound produced by pronouncing the words "Bob White." This call may be easily imitated by whistling, so as to deceive the bird itself, and bring it near. While uttering this, he is usually perched on a rail of the fence, or on a low limb of an apple-tree, where he will sometimes sit, repeating at short intervals "Bob White," for half an hour at a time. It, however, is only practised after pairing in the spring, and continues through the summer until about the middle of August, when it is substituted by another call, which is used by them until the time of pairing comes on again. When a covey are assembled in a thicket or corner of a field, and about to take wing, they make a low twittering sound, not unlike that of young chickens; and when the covey is dispersed, they are called together again by a loud and frequently repeated note, peculiarly expressive of tenderness and anxiety.

NEWFOUNDLAND DOG

NEWFOUNDLAND DOG.

CANIS FAMILIARIS. VAR. SENSILIS.

The variety of Dog so well known under the name of Newfoundland, has generally been considered by Naturalists as a mongrel, allied to the Esquimaux and Indian; but this opinion is evidently erroneous, as he differs from those varieties in the form of his head, and the general robustness of his figure. When full bred and uncontaminated by the blood of any inferior variety, he is certainly the most imposing and noble of the canine race. Although, at first sight, his great size and strength convey a sensation of fear, the mild and expressive character of his countenance manifests that ferocity is far from being a predominant or distinguishing trait of his character.

Extremely docile and affectionate, this Dog may be taught to perform actions which appear almost incredible, and which, seemingly, require no slight exercise of the reasoning faculties. Equally sagacious as persevering, he never relinquishes an undertaking as long as there remains the most distant hope of success. He seldom or ever offers offence, but will not receive an insult or injury with impunity. The great pliability of his temper, peculiarly fits him for the use of man, as he never shrinks from any task that may be assigned him, but undertakes it with an ardour proportioned to the difficulty of the execution.

The Newfoundland Dog is habitually used in its native country, for the purposes of draught. They are easily broken in, and soon inured to the trammels of harness; three, four, or five are used in a sledge or other vehicle, and will convey a load of some hundreds weight for many miles with great ease. This, when once instructed in and accustomed to the road, they will do without any supervision; and having delivered the load with which they have been entrusted, will return to the residence of their master, to receive their accustomed food, which generally consists of fish, either fresh or in a dried state, of both of which they are said to be extremely fond. Captain Brown states, that in 1810, it was computed that there were upwards of two thousand of these Dogs, at and in the vicinity of St. John's, Newfoundland. They are left to shift for themselves during the whole summer, and are not only troublesome to the inhabitants, but become absolute nuisances, from starvation and disease. Contrary to their natural disposition, where properly taken care of, under these circumstances, they assemble in packs and prowl about like wolves for their prey, destroying sheep, poultry, and every thing eatable within their reach. When the fishing season is over, and their inhuman masters again require their services, they are reclaimed, and submit with cheerfulness to the tasks which are assigned them. The same author states, that this reclamation always gives rise to much confusion and litigation, the value of these periodically deserted animals being estimated at from two to eight pounds each.

The qualifications of this Dog are not, however, confined to drawing burdens; as a watch Dog he is far more intelligent, and more to be depended on than the mastiff; and his services on navigable rivers are unequalled by any other of the species; he has even been broken in as a pointer, his sagacity and docility rendering his training an easy task.

There are, however, some faults to which he is unfortunately too prone;—he is a most implacable enemy to sheep; when engaged in chase of a flock of these animals, he generally singles out one of them, and if not prevented, which is no easy task, will never relinquish the pursuit until he has attained and mastered his victim. He always aims at the throat, but after having sucked the blood, leaves the carcass. He is, also, but too often inclined to be jealous of attentions paid by his master, either to other Dogs, or even to children, of this disposition we are acquainted with many instances.

The Newfoundland Dog in his native country, seldom barks, and that, only when much provoked. His utterance appears an unnatural exertion, producing a noise between a bark and a growl. His well known partiality for water, in which he appears in his proper element, diving and keeping beneath the surface for a considerable time, need not be commented on. The generality of the Dogs known under the name of Newfoundland, both in England and this country, are only half bred.

* Biographical Sketches and Authentic Anecdotes of Dogs, p. 198.

1. TROUT OF SILVER LAKE, DRAWN FROM ONE 24½ INCHES LONG
2. MALE BROOK TROUT DRAWN FROM ONE 9 INCHES LONG IN SEPTEM?

COMMUNICATION FROM SUSQUEHANNA COUNTY.

WITH A DRAWING OF TROUT.

Dear E.,

I received a few days ago, from Messrs. Doughty, the four numbers which they have published of their " Cabinet of Natural History and American Rural Sports," accompanied by a letter, which is entitled to a very courteous answer. They suppose that I could render them some assistance in their work; but what time have I to write, except, *currente calamo*, in the way I usually talk to you, pen in hand? I am not acquainted, personally, with either of those gentlemen; but I know perfectly well the style and manner of one of them, in his beautiful landscapes, and could point out one of his pieces among an hundred others. I wish the editors every success which they can desire; but how can I assist them in their present work? To be sure, I could tell some hunting stories for their book; but many around you could do the same, as all our countrymen are marksmen; yet, it is probable, that, of your citizen-shooters, the most expert at bagging woodcock and snipe, have never shot, as I have, an elk when at his full long trot, just as, from left to right, he crossed a small opening in the thicket, with a rifle ball, so exactly through the heart, as to bleed him to death before he could take twenty steps after the trigger was drawn; and then, with the assistance of a companion of the forest, stretched his skin on a pole, attached to two forked sticks, in time to form a shelter from a severe thunder storm, and couched myself, dry and comfortable, under it, while a deluge of rain fell unceasingly throughout the ensuing night. And, perhaps, you have no one near you, unless it may be Mr. T. R. Peale, who could say, as I could, that he eat a slice of a buffalo, admirably roasted, in fifteen minutes after the rifle was discharged which killed the animal. But Mr. P. must know how expeditiously hungry hunters can prepare a meal, without thinking of Macbeths advice,

> " If it were done, when 'tis done, then 'twere well
> It were done quickly,"

which, I believe, has been quoted in the *Cours Gastronomique*. How well Peale or Doughty could sketch the scene! One person is kindling a fire of dry sticks and leaves; another, having cut the skin just over the hump, is slicing with his scalping knife, that delicate morsel so well known to all hunters in the " far west;" while a third is employed in fixing the pieces on slender rods, like skewers, and sticking one end into the ground, the other being sloped at a proper angle to the clear blaze, and almost touching the flame. I should like to know which of your *restaurateurs* could furnish a dish equal to that repast—the side of the piece sliced away, when roasted to the depth of half an inch, and while that was, as novel writers say, " discussed," a new surface was presented to the fire—the noble animal that furnished the meal, lying invitingly by the side of the party, his dark head with its curled hair and short horns, presenting, like the black bull's head of Ravenswood, with his " I bide my time;" but serving as a better omen to the partakers of the feast. Some fastidious persons may turn from this as an Abyssinian repast: but there is no squeamishness of that kind to be found in the prairies. Ask Mr. T. R. P. whose looks bespeak him a very gentlemanly as well as amiable man, what he thinks of the relish of the buffalo hump, eaten in that way, in the western prairies. I assure you, that it would not require the appetite of Gudgel, the fat caterer for the Abbey, in the Hunt of Gildon. The boar Crowdie would have been nothing to the bos ferus— the *bos ferus!* why, that is the phrase of Cooper's Dr. Battius in his prairie! What an abominable caricature he has made of that Dr. Bat! a " Vespertilio horribilis," indeed! I am mortified and vexed at Cooper for losing so fine an opportunity of displaying a naturalist in all his glory. How a botanist might have raved! How a geologist might have ranted!—and yet, all been true to nature. Most absurd Dr. Bat! Cooper would never have suffered you on shipboard; or if by any means you had got there, long Tom Coffin would have thrown you overboard with as little compunction as he would feel at harpooning a whale.

But how I have wandered! I began this with the intention of sending you for " The Cabinet," a drawing by a young lady of your acquaintance, of the particular kind of Trout found in Silver Lake, and, so far as I know, to be found in Pennsylvania only in this and another lake, about three miles from it. I believe this species has not been described in any work on Ichthyology. It is not among the sixty-two varieties of Salmo, described by Shaw. Le Sieur knew it not. But as I think that the conductors of " The Cabinet of Rural Sports" do not desire to load their work with names in " heathen Greek," nor care about the difference between a malacoterygian and an acanthopterian; nor between the chondropterygian and the branchrostegous, I shall say nothing on that subject. The drawing will describe the species very exactly. You know its *habitat*, and can say that this fine variety of the finest genus of fishes, lives in a lake of pure water, where it may, at its discretion, vary the temperature from that which is found near the surface, affected by the sun's rays, to that at an hundred feet depth, where, throughout the year, Fahrenheit's thermometer remains at 46°

R. H. R.

MEADOW LARK.

ALAUDA MAGNA.

[Winter Plumage.]

Linn. *Syst.* 289.—*Crescent Stare, Arct. Zool.* 330. *No.* 192.—Latham, iii. 6. *Var. A.*—*Le Fer-a-cheval, ou Merle a Collier d'Amerique,* Buff. iii. *p.* 371.—Catesb. *Car.* i. *pl.* 33.—Bartram, *p.* 290.—*Alauda magna,* Linn. *Syst.* i. *p.* 167. Ed. 10.—Gmel. *Syst.* i. *p.* 801.—*Merula Americana torquata,* Briss. *Av.* ii. *p.* 242. *No.* 15.—(Summer dress.) *Sturnus ludovicianus,* Linn. *Syst.* i. *p.* 290.—Gmel. *Syst.* i. *p.* 802.—Brisson, ii. *p.* 449. 4. *t.* 42. *f.* 1.—Lath. *Ind. Orn.* i. 323.—*Etourneau de la Louisiane.*—Buff. iii. *p.* 192.—*Pl. Enl.* 256.—J. Doughty's Collection.

Though this well-known species cannot boast of the powers of song which distinguish that "harbinger of day," the Sky Lark of Europe, yet in richness of plumage, as well as in sweetness of voice (as far as his few notes extend), he stands eminently its superior. He differs from the greater part of his tribe in wanting the long straight hind claw, which is probably the reason why he has been classed, by some late naturalists, with the Starlings. But in the particular form of his bill, in his manners, plumage, mode and place of building his nest, nature has clearly pointed out his proper family.

These birds, after the building season is over, collect in flocks; but seldom fly in a close compact body; their flight is something in the manner of the grouse and partridge, laborious and steady; sailing, and renewing the rapid action of the wings alternately. When they alight on trees or bushes, it is generally on the tops of the highest branches, whence they send forth a long, clear, and somewhat melancholy note, that, in sweetness and tenderness of expression, is not surpassed by any of our numerous warblers. This is sometimes followed by a kind of low, rapid chattering, the particular call of the female; and again the clear and plaintive strain is repeated as before. They afford tolerable good amusement to the sportsman, being most easily shot while on wing; as they frequently squat among the long grass, and spring within gunshot. The nest of this species is built generally in, or below, a thick tuft or tussock of grass; it is composed of dry grass, and fine bent laid at bottom, and wound all around, leaving an arched entrance level with the ground; the inside is lined with fine stalks of the same materials, disposed with great regularity. The eggs are four, sometimes five, white, marked with specks, and several large blotches of reddish brown, chiefly at the thick end. Their food consists of caterpillars, grub worms, beetles, and grass seeds; with a considerable proportion of gravel. Their general name is the *Meadow Lark;* among the Virginians they are usually called the *Old Field Lark.*

SNOW-BIRD.

FRINGILLA HUDSONIA.

Fringilla Hudsonia, Turton, *Syst.* i. 568.—*Emberiza hyemalis, Id.* 531.—Lath. i. 66.—Catesby, i. 36.—*Arct. Zool. p.* 359, *No.* 223.—*Passer nivalis,* Bartram, *p.* 291.—*Fringilla hyemalis,* Linn. *Syst. Ed.* 10, i. *p.* 183, 30.—J. Doughty's Collection.

This well-known species, small and insignificant as it may appear, is by far the most numerous, as well as the most extensively disseminated, of all the feathered tribes that visit us from the frozen regions of the north. Their migrations extending from the arctic circle, and probably beyond it, to the shores of the gulf of Mexico, spreading over the whole breadth of the United States, from the Atlantic Ocean to Louisiana; how much farther westward I am unable to say. About the twentieth of October, they make their first appearance in those parts of Pennsylvania east of the Alleghany mountains. At first they are most generally seen on the borders of woods, among the falling and decayed leaves, in loose flocks of thirty or forty together, always taking to the trees when disturbed. As the weather sets in colder, they approach nearer the farm-house and villages; and, on the appearance of what is usually called *falling weather,* assemble in larger flocks, and seem doubly diligent in searching for food. This increased activity is generally a sure prognostic of a storm. When deep snow covers the ground, they become almost half domesticated. They collect about the barn, stables, and other outhouses, spread over the yard, and even round the steps of the door; not only in the country and villages, but in the heart of our large cities; crowding around the threshold early in the morning, gleaning up the crumbs; appearing very lively and familiar. They have also recourse, at this severe season, when the face of the earth is shut up from them, to the seeds of many kinds of weeds, that still rise above the snow, in corners of fields, and low sheltered situations, along the borders of creeks and fences, where they associate with several species of Sparrows. They are, at this time, easily caught with almost any kind of traps; are generally fat, and, it is said, are excellent eating.

SNOW BIRD

MEADOW LARK

ROUGH BILLED PELICAN.
PELECANUS ERYTHRORYNCHOS.

P. erythrorynchos. Gmel. i. 571. No. 15.—*P. trachy-rynchos.* Latham. index, 884. Phil. Trans. vol. 54, 419.—*Rough billed Pelican.* Lath. Synops. 6. p. 586. Philadelphia Museum.

The Pelicans belong to the family of Totipalmes, Cuv. which are distinguished by having their hind toe united to the others by a continuous membrane, notwithstanding which organization, they are almost the only web footed birds which perch on trees. They almost all fly well, and have short legs.

The most remarkable peculiarity of these birds, is the bag or pouch attached to the lower mandible. This bag, when empty, the bird has the power of contracting into a very small compass, and of wrinkling it up until it scarcely hangs below the bill, though when fully extended, it is of an enormous size; it may be considered as its crop, as it serves all the purposes of that receptacle, and from being placed at the commencement, instead of the termination of the gullet, it enables them to retain food in it for a considerable time, without becoming altered. When in pursuit of prey, the Pelican stows its spoils in this pouch, and when it is full, retires to the shore to devour the fruits of its industry at leisure. In this manner also, the female carries food for her young, and when disgorging it, presses the bottom of the sac upon her breast, and thus discharges its contents. This mode of procedure has, in all probability, given rise to the poetic fable of her opening her breast, and feeding her young on her own blood.

> And like the kind life rendering Pelican,
> Refresh them with my blood.*

Except this opinion of the ancients was founded on the circumstance we have alluded to, we cannot comprehend how they could have attributed to this stupid bird, the admirable qualities and maternal affections for which it was celebrated among them. When the membrane of which this pouch is composed is carefully prepared, it becomes as soft as silk, and is sometimes embroidered for work bags or purses. It is also used for tobacco pouches and shot bags, and among the negroes in the West Indies, it is thought that slippers formed from it are an infallible remedy against the gout; as well as convulsions in children.

These birds are said to be torpid and inactive to the last degree, so that nothing can exceed their indolence but their gluttony, and the powerful stimulus of hunger is necessary to excite them to exertion. They however, fly well, and can remain on the wing for a long time, hovering over the surface of the sea at a considerable height, until they perceive a fish near the surface, when they dart down with great swiftness, and seldom fail in seizing it. They all swim with equal celerity, and dive with adroitness. It is also said by some authors,† that these birds unite in flocks for the purpose of taking their prey, forming a circle, and swimming towards its centre. When they have contracted the space sufficiently, at a certain signal they all strike the water with their wings, thus frightening the fish to such a degree, that they fall an easy prey to their insatiable pursuers. These manœuvres take place during the morning and evening, as at these times the fish approach the surface of the water.

At night, when their labours are over, and they have become glutted with food, they retire some distance from the shore, and remain perched on trees till the next day calls for a renewal of their exertions. Here also they repose during most part of the day, sitting in a solemn and awkward posture, looking as if they were half asleep. Their attitude is with the head resting upon the pouch, and this closely applied to the breast. Thus they spend their life between sleeping and eating, never breaking their repose till the calls of hunger render it indispensably necessary to fill their magazine for a fresh meal. Although their usual and favourite food is fish, when this fails them, they satisfy their appetite with reptiles and small quadrupeds.

These birds are easily tamed, but they are useless and disagreeable domestics, as their insatiable gluttony renders it difficult to supply them with a sufficiency of food, and their flesh is so unsavoury and rank, as never to be eaten except from dire necessity; it is probable, however, that they might be trained for the purposes of fishing, in the same manner as the cormorant; indeed, one writer assures us that he saw a Pelican in South America, that was under such command, as to go off in the morning and return before night, with its pouch distended with prey, part of which it was made to disgorge, and the remainder it was permitted to retain as a reward. Clavigero, in his History of Mexico, also states, that the Indians, in order to procure a supply of fish without any trouble, break the wings of a live Pelican, and after tying the bird to a tree, conceal themselves near the place; the screams of the suffering bird attract other Pelicans to the place, who, he says, throw up a portion of the provisions from their pouch for their imprisoned companion; as soon as the savages perceive this to be done, they rush to the spot, and after leaving a little for the bird, carry off the remainder.

* Hamlet. Act 4. Sc. 5. † Descourtilz Voyages, d'un naturaliste. t. ii. p. 241.

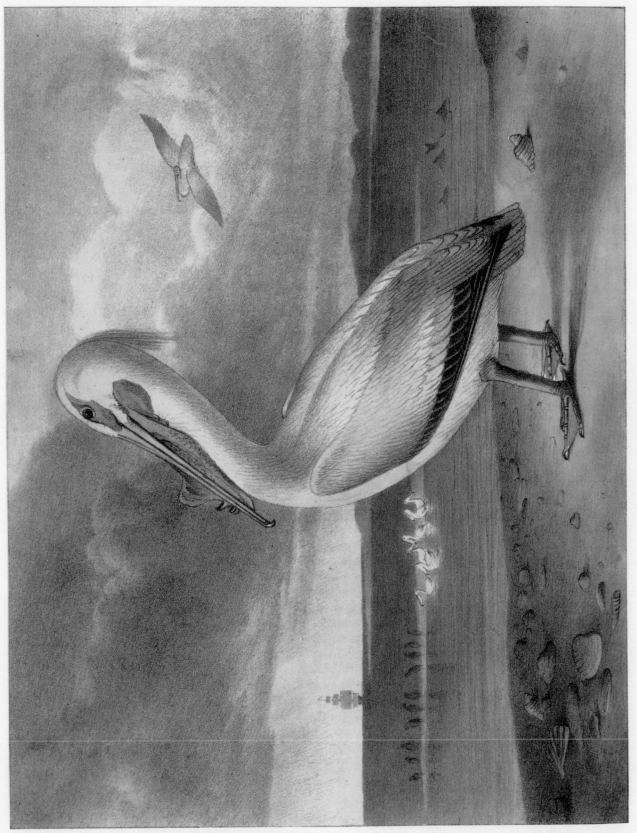

ROUGH BILLED PELICAN

25

PRAIRIE WOLVES

PRAIRIE WOLF.

CANIS LATRANS.

Small Wolf. Du Pratz, *Louisiana*, vol. ii. p. 54.—
Prairie Wolf. Lewis & Clark.—*Canis latrans.*
Say, *Expedition to the Rocky Mountains*, i. p. 168.
Richardson, *Faun. Am. bor.* 73.—*Barking Wolf.*
Godman, i. p. 260.—*Philadelphia Museum.*

The Prairie Wolf appears to have been well known to
Indian traders, and by them distinguished from its kindred
species, long before it was recognized by naturalists. Dr.
Richardson states, that skins of this animal have always
formed part of the Hudson Bay Company's importations,
under the title of *cased wolves;* so called because they are
not split open like the skins of larger animals, but stripped
off and inverted as those of the fox and rabbit.

These animals differ exceedingly in their markings and
general colour, some specimens not having the brown tints,
but being almost wholly of a grey hue, with an intermix-
ture of black in irregular spots and lines; other individuals
have a broad black mark on the shins of the fore legs, like
the European wolf. Our representation is taken from well-
preserved specimens in the Philadelphia Museum, obtained
by Mr. T. R. Peale, whilst attached to the Expedition to
the Rocky Mountains, under the command of Major Long.

The Prairie Wolf is about three feet and a half in length,
including the tail, which is about one foot. The ears are
four inches in height from the top of the head. The extremity of the trunk of the tail, reaches the projection of the
os calcis, when the leg is extended. They bear so strong
a resemblance to the domestic dog, so common in the Indian villages, that Mr. Say is of opinion they are the original stock from whence the latter is derived. Their
bark also is very similar to that of the dog; in fact the first
two or three notes cannot be distinguished from those of a
small terrier, but these are succeeded by a prolonged yell.
It was from this peculiarity of barking, that Mr. Say bestowed the specific name of *latrans* on this animal. This
species does not diffuse the offensive odour, so remarkable
in most of the other species, particularly the *nubilus* (Say.)

The Prairie Wolves occur in great numbers in the great
western plains, uniting like their brethren the jackals, in
packs for the purpose of hunting deer, which they frequently succeed in running down and killing, particularly
in a hard winter when a crust forms on the snow. It is

also said, that they will drive these animals into a lake and
remain concealed in the vicinity, watching till the exhausted
deer return, and fall an easy prey to their insatiate pursuers.
This is the more probable, as it is well known that some of
the other species of American wolves practice equally ingenious stratagems to entrap animals of superior speed. Captain Franklin gives the following interesting account of this
mode of taking their prey. "So much snow," says he,
"had fallen on the night of the 24th, that the track we intended to follow was completely covered; and our march
to-day was very fatiguing. We passed the remains of two
red deer, lying at the bases of perpendicular cliffs, from the
summits of which they had probably been forced by the
wolves. These voracious animals, who are inferior in
speed to the moose, or red deer, are said frequently to have
recourse to this expedient, in places where extensive plains
are bounded by precipitous cliffs. Whilst the deer are
quietly grazing, wolves assemble in great numbers, and,
forming a crescent, creep slowly towards the herd, so as
not to alarm them much at first; when they perceive that
they have fairly hemmed in the unsuspecting creatures,
and cut off their retreat across the plain, they move more
quickly, and with hideous yells terrify their prey, and
urge them to flight by the only open way, which is towards the precipice; appearing to know that, when the
herd is once at full speed, it is easily driven over the cliff
—the rearmost urging on those that are before. The
wolves then descend at their leisure, and feast on the
mangled carcases."

Mr. Say seems to think that they require an exercise of
all their speed, to succeed in the chase of a deer or young
buffalo, but from the statement of Dr. Richardson, and of a
writer in the Sporting Magazine, it appears, that they are
very swift and long winded, the former of these gentlemen
states, that he was informed by a trader who had resided
for many years in the Hudson Bay Company's possessions,
that the only animal which surpassed the Prairie Wolf in
swiftness, was the prong horned antelope. Notwithstanding their speed and cunning, they are often exposed to great
distress for want of food, and are reduced to the necessity
of satisfying their hunger with prairie mice, snakes, &c.,
and even of appeasing, in some degree, the cravings of appetite by distending their stomach with wild plums, and
other equally indigestible food. They have been known
to lay waste fields of corn, of which grain they are very
fond when it is in a green state. They will also venture
near the encampment of the traveller, and follow the hunter
in hopes of partaking of any offals that may be left.

WOODCOCK SHOOTING

WOODCOCK SHOOTING.

THERE is, perhaps, no sport, in this country, which occupies the attention of the shooter so much as that of hunting Woodcocks; and, as the season approaches which embraces this favourite amusement, much anxiety, preparation, and solicitude, are wasted, in anticipating the pleasure which abundance of this game produces, and, for weeks before this period arrives, the talents of all the gunsmiths are called in requisition by sportsmen, to supply any deficiencies which may be found existing in their stock of accoutrements. This undue eagerness, however, sometimes leads to great vexation and disappointment, and proves to be premature ; for, like the instability of most pleasures, the prospect of good shooting is often obscured by the storms of a single night, and those places of favourite resort by gunners, which sometimes yield rich harvests to their perseverance, are frequently rendered birdless by one heavy rain. This contingency attending Woodcock shooting, deters many from pursuing it who are extremely fond of the sport, and who prize it as superior to all others, but which circumstance alone is sufficient to bring it beneath the level of partridge shooting. In Europe, this bird is considered a great luxury, and their scarcity in England enhances their value considerably more in the eye of the sportsman, but seldom affords so much amusement as other species of game: they are, however, in this country, so plentiful, that the season for shooting them, if prudently observed, adds much to enjoyment, and constitutes an era of great importance in the sporting world.

The Woodcocks, when found in meadow land, are easy birds to shoot, and require but an indifferent shot, and slight wounds to kill them, and are therefore sought after by young sportsmen in preference to other game; for, being exceeding sluggish in their movements, they afford excellent opportunities to the beginner to exercise himself in the science of shooting. When sprung from the ground, these birds always give warning by a whistling noise with their wings, and seldom rise higher than a man's head, skimming over the ground with a slow and steady flight, to but a short distance, when they settle again in the grass—but their character is entirely changed, when the shooting is confined to bushes and thickets, as it then constitutes one of the most difficult feats to kill them, their course being very indirect and unsteady, and differing altogether from the flight of other game, springing rapidly from the ground, and rising perpendicularly, until they clear the tops of the trees or bushes, when their flight becomes more steady, but out of reach, and it requires much experience and judg-ment to embrace the proper moment to shoot before they make the twistings and turnings, in order to pass between the trees, for this most generally disconcerts every one who is not an expert shot.

The Woodcock is considered a nocturnal bird, and does all its feeding and migratory flights during this season; indeed, its sight is very imperfect in the day time, and the construction of the eye evidently unfits it for the glare of day: hence the reason why it selects, in low bushes and long grass, those sombre retreats from which it never voluntarily departs, until twilight approaches. This imperfection in sight is strikingly manifested, when driven from their seclusion, as they seldom make long flights, and are always anxious to settle immediately, as though it was painful to sustain the dazzling light of the sun, and are as likely to rush into danger as to avoid it, frequently approaching the sportsman sufficiently near to be stricken by the hand. The writer himself, during the past summer, while standing beneath the shade of a tree, observed a Woodcock settle within a few feet of him, and actually remained some seconds before it took to flight again; but this apparent stupidity is only attributable to their imperfect vision, in the day time. But no sooner do the shades of evening appear, than they sally forth, from their thousand hiding-places, to seek their food in open glades and meadows. At this time, an expert shot may reap a rich reward to his watchfulness, should he station himself near to some dense swamp, where these birds are making continual ingress and egress.

Often, in his walks at twilight, along the secluded lane or lonely meadow, does the passenger observe an object like a phantom flit before his face, or spring from his path, with a whistling noise, and is lost in the impenetrable gloom which surrounds him:—it is this lonely bird, unable to sustain that light which gives life and gaiety to other birds, now breaking forth from every opening of the woody recess, to enjoy the comfort and protection which night affords, while seeking unmolested the means of sustaining life.

Woodcocks, although migratory, remain frequently with us during the whole year—sometimes, when the streams are covered with ice, and the ground with snow; but their places of resort then, are in cedar swamps, and those springy woods, where the water never freezes, but is constantly oozing from the ground, and it appears remarkable how this bird, whose food consists altogether of worms and insects, should, at this season of the year, find means to sustain life; but Nature, ever provident in her resources, and bountiful to all her offspring, has furnished this bird with a bill whose length and delicacy of touch enables it to penetrate deeply into the earth, and draw from thence its accustomed support.

GOOSANDER   GOLDEN EYE

GOOSANDER.

MERGUS MERGANSER.

[Male.]

L'Harle, BRISS IV. *p.* 231. 1. *pl.* 22.—BUFF. VIII, *p.* 267. *pl.* 23.—*Arct. Zool. No.* 465.—LATH. *Syn.* III. *p.* 418. *Mergus Merganser*, GMEL. *Syst.* I. *p.* 544. *No.* 2.—LATH. *Ind. Orn.* p. 828, *No.* 1.—*Le Harle*, BUFF. *Pl. Enl.* 951, male.—*Grand Harle*, TEMM. *Man d'Orn.* p. 881.—*J. Doughty's Collection.*

THIS large and handsomely marked bird belongs to a genus different from that of the *Duck*, on account of the particular form and serratures of its bill. The genus is characterised as follows: "*Bill* toothed, slender, cylindrical, hooked at the point; *nostrils* small, oval, placed in the middle of the bill; *feet* four toed, the outer toe longest." Naturalists have denominated it *Merganser.* In this country, the birds composing this genus are generally known by the name of Fishermen, or Fisher ducks. The whole number of known species amount to only nine or ten, dispersed through various quarters of the world; of these, four species, of which the present is the largest, are known to inhabit the United States.

From the common habit of these birds in feeding almost entirely on fin and shell fish, their flesh is held in little estimation, being often lean and rancid, both smelling and tasting strongly of fish; but such are the various peculiarities of tastes, that persons are not wanting who pretend to consider them capital meat.

The Goosander, called by some the Water Pheasant, and by others the Sheldrake, Fisherman, Diver, &c. is a winter inhabitant only of the seashores, fresh water lakes, and rivers of the United States. They usually associate in small parties of six or eight, and are almost continually diving in search of food. In the month of April they disappear, and return again early in November. Of their particular place and manner of breeding, we have no account. Mr. Pennant observes that they continue the whole year in the Orknies, and have been shot in the Hebrides, or Western islands of Scotland, in summer. They are also found in Iceland and Greenland, and are said to breed there; some asserting that they build on trees; others that they make their nests among the rocks.

GOLDEN-EYE.

ANAS CLANGULA.

Le Garrot, BRISS. VI. *p.* 416. 27. *pl.* 37. *fig.* 2.—BUFF. IX. *p.* 222.—*Arct. Zool. No.* 486.—LATH. *Syn.* III. *p.* 535.—*Le Garrot*, *Pl. Enl.* 802.—*Morrillon*, *Arct. Zool.* II. *p.* 300. F.—*Br. Zool. No.* 276, 277.—LATH. *Supp.* II. *p.* 535, *No.* 26,—*Ind. Orn.* p. 867, *No.* 87; *A. glancion, Id. p.* 868, *No.* 88.—GMEL. *Syst.* I. *p.* 523, *No.* 23; *Id. p.* 525, *No.* 26.—TEMM. *Man. d'Orn.* I. *p.* 870.—BEWICK, II. *p.* 330.—*J. Doughty's Collection.*

THIS Duck is well known in Europe, and in various regions of the United States, both along the seacoast and about the lakes and rivers of the interior. It associates in small parties, and may easily be known by the vigorous whistling of its wings, as it passes through the air. It swims and dives well; but seldom walks on shore, and then in a waddling awkward manner. Feeding chiefly on shell fish, small fry, &c. their flesh is less esteemed than that of the preceding. In the United States they are only winter visitors, leaving us again in the month of April, being then on their passage to the north to breed. They are said to build, like the wood duck, in hollow trees.

The conformation of the trachea, or windpipe of the male of this species, is singular. Nearly about its middle it swells out to at least five times its common diameter, the concentric hoops or rings, of which this part is formed, falling obliquely into one another when the windpipe is relaxed; but when stretched, this part swells out to its full size, rings being then drawn apart; this expansion extends for about three inches; three more below this it again forms itself into a hard cartilaginous shell, of an irregular figure, and nearly as large as a walnut; from the bottom of this labyrinth, as it has been called, the trachea branches off to the two lobes of the lungs; that branch which goes to the left lobe being three times the diameter of the right. The female has nothing of all this. The intestines measure five feet in length, and are large and thick.

GRIZZLY BEARS

GRISLY BEAR.

URSUS HORRIBILIS..

Grisly Bear. MACKENZIE, *voyages &c.* 160.—*Grisly, brown, white and variegated Bear.* LEWIS & CLARK. —*Grizzly Bear.* WARDEN's *United States.* GODMAN *Nat. Hist.* i. p. 131.—*Ursus Horribilis.* ORD. SAY. *Expedit. to the Rocky Mountains,* ii. p. 52.—*Ursus Cinereus.* DESM. *Mammal.*—*Ursus Ferox.* LEWIS & CLARK. RICHARDSON. *Faun. Am. bor.* 24.—*Ursus Candescens.* HAMILTON SMITH. GRIFFITH's and KING. ii. p. 229. & 5. No. 320.—PEALE's MUSEUM.

The Grisly Bear is indubitably the most formidable and powerful of all the quadrupeds which inhabit the northern regions of the American continent ; and it is not to be wondered at, that a victory over an animal of such strength and ferocity, should be considered of such importance among the native tribes inhabiting the inhospitable regions where it is now found.

The accounts of the dimensions of these animals differ ; they are reported to attain a weight exceeding 800 pounds, and Lewis and Clark mention one that measured nine feet in length, and add, that they had seen a still larger one, but do not give its dimensions. Governor Clinton received intelligence of one said to be fourteen feet long, but even admitting that there was no exaggeration in this statement, it is probable that the admeasurements were taken from a skin which had been stretched. The dimensions given by Mr. Say, which were taken from the two prepared specimens in the Philadelphia Museum, by no means give an idea of the size to which this animal attains, as these individuals died before they had reached their full growth ; these measurements are however valuable as presenting a correct view of the proportions of different parts of the body.

Of the strength of this Bear, some estimation may be formed, from its having been known to drag the carcass of a Buffalo, weighing at least a thousand pounds, to a considerable distance. Dr. Richardson gives the following story which he says is well authenticated. "A party of voyagers, who had been employed all day in tracking a canoe up the Saskatchewan, had seated themselves in the twilight by a fire, and were busy in preparing their supper, when a large Grisly Bear sprung over their canoe that was tilted behind them, and seizing one of the party by the shoulder carried him off. The rest all fled in terror with the exception of a Metif, named Bourasso, who grasping his gun followed the Bear as it was retreating leisurely with its prey. He called to his unfortunate comrade that he was afraid of hitting him, if he fired at the Bear, but the latter entreated him to fire immediately, without hesitation, as the Bear, was squeezing him to death, on this he took a deliberate aim, and discharged his piece into the body of the Bear, which instantly dropped its prey to pursue Bourasso. He escaped with difficulty, and the Bear ultimately retreated to a thicket, where it was supposed to have died, but the curiosity of the party not being a match for their fears, the fact of its decease was not ascertained. The man who was rescued had his arm fractured, and was otherwise severely bitten by the Bear, but finally recovered."*

The Grisly Bear appears to be very tenacious of life. Mr. Say informs us, one lived two hours, after having been shot through the lungs, and whilst in this state, prepared a bed for himself in the earth, two feet deep, and five feet long, having previously run a mile and a half. It is, in fact, very difficult to kill one of these animals by a single shot, except the ball penetrates the brain or the heart, and this seldom is effected from the form of the skull in the first case, and the thick coat of hair in the latter. To give a better idea of the danger attendant on the chase of these bears, we select the following instance from Lewis and Clark:

One evening the men in the hindmost of one of Lewis and Clark's canoes perceived one of those Bears lying in the open ground about three hundred paces from the river, and six of them, who were all good hunters, went to attack him. Concealing themselves by a small eminence, they were able to approach within forty paces unperceived; four of the hunters now fired, and each lodged a ball in his body, two of which passed directly through the lungs. The Bear sprang up and ran furiously with open mouth upon them ; two of the hunters, who had reserved their fire, gave him two additional wounds, and one breaking his shoulder-blade, somewhat retarded his motions. Before they could again load their guns, he came so close on them, that they were obliged to run towards the river, and before they had gained it, the Bear had almost overtaken them. Two men jumped into the canoe; the other four separated, and concealing themselves among the willows, fired as fast as they could load their pieces. Several times the Bear was struck, but each shot seemed only to direct his fury towards the hunter; at last he pursued them so closely that they threw aside their guns and pouches, and jumped down a perpendicular bank, twenty feet high, into the river. The Bear sprang after them, and was very near the hindmost man, when one of the hunters on shore, shot him through the head, and finally killed him. On examination, it was found that eight balls had passed through his body in different directions.

*Richardson. Faun. Am. Bor. 27.

33

BLUE BIRD   ROBIN

ROBIN.

TURDUS MIGRATORIUS.

Linn. *Syst.* i, *p.* 292, 6.—*Turdus Canadensis,* Briss. ii, *p.* 225, 9.—*La Litorne de Canada,* Buff. iii, *p.* 307.—*Grive de Canada, Pl. Enl.* 556, 1.—*Fieldfare of Carolina,* Cat. *Car.* 1, 29.—*Red-breasted Thrush, Arct. Zool.* ii, *No.* 196.—Lath. *Syn.* ii, *p.* 26.—Bartram, *p.* 290.—J. Doughty's *collection.*

The Robin builds a large nest, often on an apple tree, plasters it in the inside with mud, and lines it with hay or fine grass. The female lays five eggs of a beautiful sea green. Their principal food is berries, worms and catterpillars.

The Robin is one of our earliest songsters; even in March, while snow yet dapples the fields, and flocks of them are dispersed about, some few will mount a post or stake of the fence, and make short and frequent attempts at their song. Early in April, they are only to be seen in pairs, and deliver their notes with great earnestness, from the top of some tree detached from the woods. This song has some resemblance to, and indeed is no bad imitation of the notes of the Thrush or Thrasher (*Turdus rufus*); but if deficient in point of execution, he possesses more simplicity; and makes up in zeal what he wants in talent; so that the notes of the Robin, in spring, are universally known, and as universally beloved. They are as it were the prelude to the grand general concert, that is about to burst upon us from woods, fields, and thickets, whitened with blossoms, and breathing fragrance. By the usual association of ideas, we therefore listen with more pleasure to this cheerful bird than to many others possessed of far superior powers, and much greater variety. Even his nest is held more sacred among school boys than that of some others; and while they will exult in plundering a Jay's or a Cat-bird's, a general sentiment of respect prevails on the discovery of a Robin's. Whether he owes not some little of this veneration to the well known and long established character of his namesake in Britain, by a like association of ideas, I will not pretend to determine. He possesses a good deal of his suavity of manners, and almost always seeks shelter for his young in summer, and subsistence for himself in the extremes of winter, near the habitations of man.

BLUE BIRD.

S. SIALIS.

Le Rouge gorge bleu, Buffon, v. 212, *Pl. Enl.* 390.—*Blue. Warbler,* Lath. ii, 446.—Catesb. i, 47.—*Motacilla sialis,* Linn. *Syst.* 336.—Bartram, *p.* 291.—*Motacilla sialis,* Linn. *Syst.* i, *p.* 187, Ed. 10.—Gmel. *Syst.* i, *p.* 989.—*Sylvia sialis,* Lath. *Ind. Orn.* ii, 522.—Vieillot, *Otis. de l'Am. Sept. pl.* 101, *male;* 102, *female;* 103, *young.*—*La Gorge rouge de la Caroline,* Buff. *Pl. Enl.* 396, *fig.* 1, *male; fig.* 2, *female.*—J. Doughty's *collection.*

The pleasing manners and sociable disposition of this little bird entitle him to particular notice. As one of the first messengers of spring, bringing the charming tidings to our very doors, he bears his own recommendation always along with him, and meets with a hearty welcome from every body.

Though generally accounted a bird of passage, yet so early as the middle of February, if the weather be open, he usually makes his appearance about his old haunts, the barn, orchard and fence posts. Storms and deep snows sometimes succeeding, he disappears for a time; but about the middle of March is again seen, accompanied by his mate, visiting the box in the garden, or the hole in the old appletree, the cradle of some generations of his ancestors. "When he first begins his amours," says a curious and correct observer, "it is pleasing to behold his courtship, his solicitude to please and to secure the favour of his beloved female. He uses the tenderest expressions, sits close by her, caresses and sings to her his most endearing warblings. When seated together, if he espies an insect delicious to her taste, he takes it up, flies with it to her, spreads his wing over her and puts it in her mouth."* If a rival makes his appearance, (for they are ardent in their loves), he quits her in a moment, attacks and pursues the intruder, as he shifts from place to place, in tones that bespeak the jealousy of his affection, conducts him with many reproofs beyond the extremities of his territory, and returns to warble out his transports of triumph beside his beloved mate. The preliminaries being thus settled, and the spot fixed on, they begin to clean out the old nest, and the rubbish of the former year, and to prepare for the reception of their future offspring.

---

* Letter from Mr. William Bartram to the author.

WOODCOCK.

SCOLOPAX MINOR.

Arct. Zool. p. 463, No. 365.—Turt. *Syst.* 396. *Scolopax minor,* Lath. *Ind. Orn.* p. 714, *No. 2. Gen. Syn.* 3, p. 131.—J. Doughty's *Collection.*

This bird is universally known to our sportsmen. It arrives in Pennsylvania early in March, sometimes sooner; and I doubt not but in mild winters some few remain with us the whole of that season. During the day, they keep to the woods and thickets, and at the approach of evening seek the springs, and open watery places, to feed in. They soon disperse themselves over the country to breed. About the beginning of July, particularly in long-continued hot weather, they descend to the marshy shores of our large rivers, their favourite springs and watery recesses, inland, being chiefly dried up. To the former of these retreats they are pursued by the merciless sportsman, flushed by dogs, and shot down in great numbers. This species of amusement, when eagerly followed, is still more laborious and fatiguing than that of Snipe-shooting; and from the nature of the ground, or cripple as it is usually called, *viz.* deep mire, intersected with old logs, which are covered and hid from sight by high reeds, weeds, and alder bushes, the best dogs are soon tired out; and it is customary with sportsmen, who regularly pursue this diversion, to have two sets of dogs, to relieve each other alternately.

The Woodcock is properly a nocturnal bird, feeding chiefly at night, and seldom stirring about till after sunset. At such times, as well as in the early part of the morning, particularly in spring, he rises by a kind of spiral course, to a considerable height in the air, uttering at times a sudden *quack,* till having gained his utmost height, he hovers around in a wild, irregular manner, making a sort of murmuring sound; then descends with rapidity as he rose. When uttering his common note on the ground, he seems to do it with difficulty, throwing his head towards the earth, and frequently jetting up his tail. These notes and manœuvres are most usual in spring, and are the call of the male to his favourite female. Their food consists of various larvæ, and other aquatic worms, for which, during the evening, they are almost continually turning over the leaves with their bill, or searching in the bogs. Their flesh is reckoned delicious, and prized highly. They remain with us till late in autumn; and on the falling of the first snows, descend from the ranges of the Alleghany, to the lower parts of the country, in great numbers; soon after which, *viz.* in November, they move off to the south.

This bird, in its general figure and manners, greatly resembles the Woodcock of Europe, but is considerably less, and very differently marked below, being an entirely distinct species. A few traits will clearly point out their differences. The lower parts of the European Woodcock are thickly barred with dusky waved lines, on a yellowish white ground. The present species has those parts of a bright ferruginous. The male of the American species weighs from five to six ounces, the female eight: the European twelve. The European Woodcock makes its first appearance in Britain in October and November, that country being in fact only its winter quarters; for early in March they move off to the northern parts of the continent to breed. The American species, on the contrary, winters in countries south of the United States, arrives here early in March, extends its migrations as far, at least, as the river St. Lawrence, breeds in all the intermediate places, and retires again to the south on the approach of winter. The one migrates from the torrid to the temperate regions; the other from the temperate to the arctic. The two birds, therefore, notwithstanding their names are the same, differ not only in size and markings, but also in native climate. Hence the absurdity of those who would persuade us, that the Woodcock of America crosses the Atlantic to Europe, and *vice versa.* These observations have been thought necessary, from the respectability of some of our own writers, who seem to have adopted this opinion.

How far to the north our Woodcock is found, I am unable to say. It is not mentioned as a bird of Hudson's Bay; and being altogether unknown in the northern parts of Europe, it is very probable that its migrations do not extend to a very high latitude; for it may be laid down as a general rule, that those birds which migrate to the arctic regions in either continent, are very often common to both. The head of the Woodcock is of singular conformation, large, somewhat triangular, and the eye fixed at a remarkable distance from the bill, and high in the head. This construction was necessary to give a greater range of vision, and to secure the eye from injury while the owner is searching in the mire. The flight of the Woodcock is slow. When flushed at any time in the woods, he rises to the height of the bushes or under wood, and almost instantly drops behind them again at a short distance, generally running off for several yards as soon as he touches the ground. The notion that there are two species of Woodcock in this country probably originated from the great difference between the male and female, the latter being considerably the larger.

GROUND SQUIRREL

GROUND SQUIRREL.

SCIURUS (TAMIAS) LYSTERI.

Sciurus Lysteri.—RAY, *Synops. Quad.* 216.—*Sciurus Striatus.* KLEIN, *Pall. Glires,* 378.—GMEL. *Schreb. tab.* 221.—*Sciurus Carolinensis,* BRISS. *Reg. An.* 155. No. 9.—*Ecureuil Suisse.*—DESM. 339, 5 *p.* 547.—*Escurieux Suisses.*—*Sagard-Theodat, Canada, P.* 746. *Ground Squirrel,* LAWSON, *Carolina, P.* 124.—*Catesby,* CAROL. *Vol.* 2. *p.* 75.—EDWARDS, *Vol.* 4, *t.* 181. KALM, *Vol.* 1. *p.* 322. *t. i.*—GODMAN, *Vol.* 2. *p.* 142. *Striped Dormouse,* PENNANT—*Arct. Zool. Vol.* 1. *p.* 126.—HACKEE, *United States.*—J. DOUGHTY's *Collection.*

THE beautiful little animal whose biography and description we are about relating, is known to most of the inabitants of the United States, being found in all districts of the country, as far north as the 50th parallel; its chief habitation, however, appears to be in the vicinage of man, although numbers may be seen on the shores of Lakes Huron and Superior. It is the first wild animal which attracts the notice of infancy, who grow to manhood with so intimate an acquaintance with it, that it is unnoticed either for its beauty, or interesting habits, because familiarity has made it common ; but in a minute investigation of its habits and properties, its beauties are more fully developed, and a close investigation of its foresight, and apparent wisdom, will lead us to admire an animal from which important instruction may be derived.

Associated with the Ground Squirrel, are many pleasing little reminiscenses, it recalls the mature mind to days of boyhood, when that period was often wasted in the idle enjoyment of persecuting this common inhabitant of the wood, when hours and days were spent in almost fruitless exertion to make it prisoner, when the country schoolboy exhausted his truant hours, in more severe labour by chasing from fence to fence, or from tree to tree, this active animal—than days of study would create, and when the rambles by the brook's margin, or through the lonely wood, were mostly enlivened by the spirited chirping of the Ground Squirrel.

Often, too, in the solitary wilds of our country, where nature appears almost forsaken of animated life, does the traveller find a companion in this pretty Squirrel, while it is passing swiftly from stone to stone, or scudding along the fences by the road side. These fences, which are commonly the ziz-zag or worm fences, afford them fine shelter from their enemies, and a secure and regular path for their fleetness.

The favourite places of resort for the Ground Squirrel are woods embedded with rocks and stones, the margin of shaded brooks or creeks, along fences, old walls, and banks adjacent to forests. They live in the ground, and their burrows, are mostly at the foot of stumps or trees, and beside rocks, extending to a considerable distance beneath the surface, having several branches from the principal passage, each of which is terminated by a store-house for their winter supplies; and, as they feed on the various kinds of nuts, the products of our forests, they deposit each in a separate cell, accumulating, through the summer and autumn, a most incredible quantity of provisions for the emergencies of winter. This provident store is never impaired, until the severities of the climate confines them to their burrows. During the summer season, they eat corn, wheat, rye, cherry-stones, acorns, &c. Their favourite food, however, is chesnuts, and in forests where these trees abound, numbers of these animals may always be found. Their burrows frequently possess two entrances, to afford them either a more easy access to their cells, or to escape more readily from their enemies.

These animals are seldom seen on trees, unless driven there for refuge, but may be found at all hours of the day, during the warm weather, sitting on the summit of some rock, stump, or fence, in a manner as represented in the plate, where, if unmolested, they will remain for hours, whistling and chattering away the tedium of a summer's day, making so much noise as to be heard from the most remote recess of the wood. Should they be intruded on at this period, their noise will cease, and after a short pause, watching the progress of the intruder, they will glide rapidly into their holes, with a shrill cry or whistle peculiar to this action. They are timid animals, and seldom wander far from their burrows, except in search of food, and, as the early morning and late evening are devoted to this purpose, it requires much wariness in the pursuer to surprise them, and if successful in doing this, they will then ascend the nearest trees, which, if somewhat detached from other trees, they are frequently captured. They are considered the most untameable of their species, and can seldom be reduced to familiarity, but will generally bite their keeper, and survive only a short time, if imprisoned.

SWANS

40

WILD SWAN.

CYGNUS FERUS.

(By John T. Sharpless, M. D.)

Anas cygnus ferus, Linn.—*Cygnus ferus*, Briss.—*Le Cygne sauvage*, Buff.—*Elk, or Hooper Swan*, Ray Whistling Swan, Lath. Pennant.—*Cygnus musicus*, Bechst.—*Swan*, Wilson's List.—*Wapa-Seu*, Indians Hud. Bay.—J. Doughty's *Collection.*

The Swan has been emphatically called the peaceful monarch of the Lake. It is undoubtedly the most beautiful of all the water-birds, whether we consider the spotless purity of its plumage, the gracefulness of its contour, or the majesty of its movements. It is in its own element alone, that it can display its charms, being extremely awkward and inelegant in all its motions when placed on its feet, but when seen peacefully engaged in the excitement of play, or calmly dressing its stainless garb in the lovely mirror on which it floats, it is one of the most agreeable and untiring ornaments in nature.

The princely magnificence of the Swan has attracted from the earliest day the attention of every admirer of the beauties of creation, and having been chosen by the ancients as the mansion of departed Poets, is sufficient evidence of their love and veneration.

" The dying Swan's last, sweetest note,"

was supposed to be the departure of the poetic spirit to happier realms, and although, to the crude ear of moderns, the dying expiration of the Swan is not wafted on the wings of melody, the change may have arisen from a vitiation of musical taste, or perhaps, as Morin says,

" The Swans that once so sweetly sang,
Sing very illy now."

About the first of September, the Swans leave the shores of the Polar sea, according to Franklin, and resort to the lakes and rivers in about the latitude of Hudson Bay, (60°) where they remain preparing for a departure for the winter, until October, when they collect in flocks of twenty or thirty, and seizing favourable weather, with the wind not opposed to the direction of their flight, they mount high in the air, form a prolonged wedge and with loud screams depart for more genial climes. When making either their semi-annual transmigration, or on shorter expeditions, an occasional scream equal to " how do you all come on behind" issues from the leader, which is almost immediately replied to by some posterior Swan with an " all's well" vociferation. When the leader of the party becomes fatigued with his extra duty of cutting the air, he falls in the rear and his neighbour takes his place. When mounted, as they sometimes are, several thousand feet above the earth, with their diminished and delicate outline hardly perceptible against the clear blue of heaven, this harsh sound softened and modulated by distance, and issuing from the immense void above, assumes a supernatural character of tone and impression, that excites, the first time heard, a strangely peculiar feeling.

In flying, these birds make a strange appearance; their long necks protrude and present, at a distance, mere lines with black points, and occupy more than one half their whole length, their heavy bodies and triangular wings seeming but mere appendages to their immense projections in front.

When thus in motion, their wings pass through so few degrees of the circle, that, unless seen horizontally, they appear almost quiescent, being widely different from the heavy semi-circular sweep of the Goose. The Swan, when migrating, with a moderate wind in his favour, and mounted high in the air, certainly travels at the rate of one hundred miles or more an hour. I have often *timed* the flight of the Goose, and found one mile a minute a common rapidity, and when the two birds, in a change of feeding ground, have been flying near each other, which I have often seen, the Swan invariably passed with nearly double the velocity.

The Swan in travelling from the northern parts of America to their winter residence, generally keep far inland, mounted above the highest peaks of the Alleghany, and rarely follow the water courses like the Goose, which usually stop on the route, particularly, if they have taken the sea board. The Swan rarely pause on their migrating flight, unless overtaken by a storm, above the reach of which occurrence, they generally soar. They have been seen following the coast in but very few instances. They arrive at their winter homes, which is a belt crossing the whole continent, and extending from the latitude of 40° to Florida, and even to the West India Islands and Mexico, in October and November, and immediately take possession of their regular feeding ground. They generally reach these places in the night, and the first signal of their arrival at their winter abode, is a general burst of melody, making the shores ring for several hours with their vociferating congratulations, whilst making amends for a long fast, and pluming their deranged feathers. From these localities, they rarely depart, unless driven farther south by intensely cold weather, until their vernal excursion. When the spring arrives, a similar collection of forces as at the north, takes place in March, and, after disturbing the tranquil bosom of the water for a night, by incessant washing and dressing, and alarming the quiet neighbourhood by a constant clatter of consulting tongues, they depart for the north about daylight with a general *feu-de-joie* of unmusical screams.

RAIL

RAIL.

RALLUS CAROLINUS.

Soree, Catesb. i. 70.—*Arct. Zool.* p. 491, *No.* 409.—*Little American Water Hen,* Edw. 144.—*Le Râl de Virginie,* Buff. viii. 165.—*Rallus Carolinus,* Lin. *Syst.* p. 153, *No.* 5, ed. 10.—*Gallinula Carolina,* Lath. *Ind. Orn.* p. 771, *No.* 17.—J. Doughty's Collection.

The natural history of the *Rail,* or as it is called in Virginia, the *Sora,* and in South Carolina the *Coot,* is, to the most of our sportsmen, involved in profound and inexplicable mystery. It comes, they know not whence; and goes, they know not whither. No one can detect their first moment of arrival; yet all at once the reedy shores, and grassy marshes, of our large rivers swarm with them, thousands being sometimes found within the space of a few acres. These, when they do venture on wing, seem to fly so feebly, and in such short fluttering flights among the reeds, as to render it highly improbable, to most people, that they could possibly make their way over an extensive tract of country. Yet, on the first smart frost that occurs, the whole suddenly disappear, as if they had never been.

To account for these extraordinary phenomena, it has been supposed, by some, that they bury themselves in the mud; but as this is every year dug into by ditchers and people employed in repairing the banks, without any of those sleepers being found, where but a few weeks before these birds were innumerable, this theory has been generally abandoned. And here their researches into this mysterious matter generally end in the common exclamation of "What can become of them!" Some profound inquirers, however, not discouraged with these difficulties, have prosecuted their researches with more success; and one of those, living a few years ago near the mouth of James river, in Virginia, where the Rail or Sora are extremely numerous, has (as I was informed on the spot) lately discovered, that they change into *frogs!* having himself found in his meadows an animal of an extraordinary kind, that appeared to be neither a Sora nor a frog; but, as he expressed it, "something between the two."

Since the above was written, I have received from Mr. George Ord, of Philadelphia, some curious particulars relative to this bird, which, as they are new, and come from a gentleman of respectability, are worthy of being recorded, and merit further investigation.

"My personal experience," says Mr. Ord, "has made me acquainted with a fact in the history of the Rail, which perhaps is not generally known; and I shall, as briefly as possible, communicate it to you. Some time in the autumn of the year 1809, as I was walking in a yard, after a severe shower of rain, I perceived the feet of a bird projecting from a spout. I pulled it out, and discovered it to be a Rail, very vigorous, and in perfect health. The bird was placed in a small room, on a gin-case; and I was amusing myself with it, when, in the act of pointing my finger at it, it suddenly sprang forward, apparently much irritated, fell to the floor, and stretching out its feet, and bending its neck, until the head nearly touched the back, became to all appearance lifeless. Thinking the fall had killed the bird, I took it up, and began to lament my rashness in provoking it. In a few minutes it again breathed; and it was some time before it perfectly recovered from the fit, into which, it now appeared evident, it had fallen. I placed the Rail in a room, wherein Canary birds were confined; and resolved that, on the succeeding day, I would endeavour to discover whether or not the passion of anger had produced the fit. I entered the room at the appointed time, and approached the bird, which had retired, on beholding me, in a sullen humour, to a corner. On pointing my finger at it, its feathers were immediately ruffled; and in an instant it sprang forward, as in the first instance, and fell into a similar fit. The following day the experiment was repeated, with the like effect. In the autumn of 1811, as I was shooting amongst the reeds, I perceived a Rail rise but a few feet before my batteau. The bird had risen about a yard when it became entangled in the tops of a small bunch of reeds, and immediately fell. Its feet and neck were extended, as in the instances above mentioned; and before it had time to recover, I killed it. Some few days afterwards, as a friend and I were shooting in the same place, he killed a Rail, and, as we approached the spot to pick it up, another was perceived, not a foot off, in a fit. I took up the bird, and placed it in the crown of my hat. In a few moments it revived, and was as vigorous as ever. These facts go to prove, that the Rail is subject to gusts of passion, which operate to so violent a degree as to produce a disease, similar in its effects so epilepsy. I leave the explication of the phenomenon to those pathologists who are competent and willing to investigate it. It may be worthy of remark, that the birds affected as described, were all females of the *Rallus Carolinus,* or Common Rail."

AMERICAN ARGALI

AMERICAN ARGALI.

OVIS MONTANA.

[Male and Female.]

White Buffalo.—Mackenzie, Voyages *Mountain Ram.* M'Gillivray.—New York Med. Repos. vol. vi. *Big Horn.*—Lewis and Clark. *Ovis Montana.*—Desmarest, Mamm. Cuvier, Reg. an. Richardson, Faun. am. bor. *Ovis Ammon.*—Godman. Harlan. *Ovis Ammon var Pygargus.*—Griffith, An. King. *Rocky Mountain Sheep.*—Warden. Unit. St.—Philadelphia Museum.

To none of the domestic animals is mankind more indebted for the comforts and luxuries of civilized life than to this quadruped; others may excel it in strength, speed, and dignity of character, but were we to be deprived of the services of any of our attendants among the inferior animals, we would in all probability find that those of the Sheep would be as severely felt as any of the others. The inoffensive and mild character of these animals, when under the control of man, is so well known as to have descended into a proverb. But when ranging in flocks over the extensive tracts devoted to them in many countries, and where they seldom depend on the aid of the shepherd, they display very different characteristics. Here, being obliged to depend on their own resources, when threatened with an attack, they show a courage and resolution which is generally supposed to be foreign to their nature. Thus, a ram will boldly meet and drive off a dog or fox, and where the danger is more alarming, the whole flock unites for common defence, drawing up in a circle, placing the young and females in the centre, whilst the old males present an armed front to the assailant that is not to be easily vanquished.

The benefits which this animal bestows on mankind are exceedingly numerous. Its horns, its flesh, its tallow, and even its bowels, all furnish articles of great utility. The horns are manufactured into various articles, as spoons, buttons, cups, &c. The flesh is too well known, as one of our most valuable meats, to require notice. The manufacture of its wool into cloths has long formed the principal source of wealth to England, and, in all probability, will become equally so in this country. The skin, is prepared into leather, for inferior kinds of shoes, for the coverings of books, for gloves, and into parchment. The entrails, by a proper preparation, form those strings for musical instruments known under the name of catgut. The bones are employed for a variety of purposes in the arts. The milk has more consistence than that of the cow, but is embued with a rank taste; the cheese made from it, though rich, is necessarily strong.

The American Argali inhabits the mountainous regions of country situated in the western part of North America, not occurring further eastward than the delivity of the Rocky mountains. They generally frequent the highest parts of this chain which produce any vegetation, but sometimes descend to feed in the valleys, though on the least alarm, they fly for shelter to their native precipices, where the hunter finds it difficult to follow them. Mr. Drummond informed Dr. Richardson, that in the retired parts of the mountains, where they had seldom been alarmed by hunters, that he found but little difficulty in approaching them; though in spots where they had been often fired at, that they were extremely shy, alarming their companions with a hissing noise, like the Chamois.

They assemble in flocks consisting of various numbers, though seldom exceeding thirty, the young rams and the females hording together in the winter and spring. The female brings forth in June or July, when she retires with her young to the most inaccessible situations.

Mr. M'Gillivray says, the appearance of this animal, though rather clumsy, is expressive of great activity and strength, and his agility in traversing the rugged and almost impassable spots he inhabits is truly surprising, bounding from rock to rock, like the Ibex. " Frequently," he continues, " I have been entertained with a view of one of them, looking over the brink of a precipice several hundred yards above my head, scarcely appearing bigger than a crow, and bidding defiance to all approach. These frightful situations are quite natural to them. They run up declivities of hard snow or rough ice with facility. Pursuing them in these situations, I have been obliged to cut steps with my knife, where they passed without difficulty. Sometimes you think their progress is stopped by a chasm or projecting rock; but if you attempt too near an approach, at one bound they are out of your reach."

Their favourite places of resort are the grassy knolls, situated amidst craggy rocks, which serve them as retreats when pursued by an enemy. Mr. Drummond also states, that they are accustomed to pay daily visits to certain caves in the mountains, which afford a saline efflorescence, of which, like most other ruminating animals, they are very fond.

All those who have eaten of the flesh of these animals, particularly of the female and young male, agree that it is extremely delicate, and preferable to the finest venison; even the Indians, who live entirely on animal food, may be supposed epicures in the choice of flesh, agree that the flesh of the Argali is the sweetest feast in the forest.

VARYING HARE

46

AMERICAN VARYING HARE.

LEPUS VIRGINIANUS.—Harlan.

Varying Hare, Pennant Quad. Warden Descrip. U. S. v. p. 635. Lewis & Clarke, 2. p. 178. *Lepus Virginianus,* Harlan. Faun. am. 196, 300. *Prairie Hare,* Richardson, Faun. am. bor.—Philadelphia Museum.

Few of the genera of quadrupeds present more obstacles to the naturalist, than that of Lepus; among the species of which there are so many points of similarity and almost identity, that it is a task of no slight difficulty to distinguish whether the differential characters which have been assigned to them, are really specific, or only arise from the modifying influence of climate and habitat. But although the several species of this genus are so analogous as to constitute one of the most natural groups of the mammalia, they are spread over a wide extent of the globe, exhibiting, however, in every country, the same characteristics. When we consider the great and almost incredible changes that are wrought in the external configuration and habits of animals by change of residence, and the effects of domestication, it must be evident that it is often impossible to determine whether the apparent differences between animals arise from their descent from various parent stocks, or have been produced by the gradual operation of extrinsic causes. Thus, when the natural history of any one of our domestic animals, as the sheep for example, is sufficiently known; when we find, on its transportation from one climate to another, that changes are produced, apparently amounting to specific differences, it becomes exceedingly difficult to assign any limits to this operation of nature, and to decide, in an absolute manner, between the analogy and affinity of animals. These observations apply with great force to the genus under consideration, from the striking similarity that exists between the species composing it, species, however, it should be recollected, sanctioned by the highest names in zoology.

As the resemblance of the various species to the common type is almost as strong in their habits and manners as in external characters, what we shall notice in speaking of the genus is applicable, in a great measure, to the individual which now engages our attention.

There is one very remarkable anatomical peculiarity in this genus; the females are furnished with a double matrix, so that two contemporaneous fecundations can go on together; this peculiarity of form also accounts for these animals being so extremely prolific. They are capable of reproduction at a very early age, and produce young every thirty days, having from two to five at a birth.

According to the Mosaic ordinances, these animals are placed among the ruminants. This arose, perhaps, from the stomach appearing double, owing to a peculiar fold in it; added to which, the coecum is so large that, in the infancy of anatomical knowledge, it might readily have been mistaken for a second stomach; the Hare genus have also the habit of keeping their under lip in constant motion, giving the semblance of rumination. But, although forbidden to be eaten by the Jews, and even by the ancient Britons, the flesh of the Hare appears to have been held in great esteem by the epicures of Rome; thus, Martial says, *" Inter quadrupedes gloria prima Lepus,"* and Horace, who is no slight authority as regards the pleasures of the table, gives it as his opinion, that every man of taste must prefer the fore leg: *" Fecunditur Leporis sapiens sectabitur armos."*

The eye of the Hare has no accessory organ, and the pupil is elongated horizontally; their nostrils are nearly circular, and almost hidden in a fold, so that they can be closed. The ears of all the species are very large, and are also capable of being closed at the will of the animal. The voice of these animals is seldom or never heard, except when they are irritated or wounded, when they utter a loud piercing cry, bearing some resemblance to that of a child in pain. Although exceedingly timid and watchful, the Hare is capable of being domesticated, and even taught a variety of tricks. One was exhibited in London, some time since, which could play on the tambourine, discharge a pistol, and perform a variety of other feats of as strange a character for an animal of so fearful a disposition.

From the great length of the hinder legs, the gait of the Hare is a succession of leaps, or an interrupted gallop; like all animals of this conformation they sit on the tarsi of the hinder feet, and use the anterior extremities to convey food to the mouth, to cleanse their fur, &c. They drink by lapping. This length of the hinder limbs also enables them to ascend declivities with great speed. They feed on vegetables, and are very destructive to bark of young trees.

One of the most remarkable peculiarities of this genus is the difference of habits between some of the species, closely allied as they are in their physical appearance. Thus, the Rabbit and the Hare, although furnished with analogous organs, and inhabiting in many instances the same countries, manifest the greatest aversion for each other, a hatred which M. F. Cuvier asserts nothing can obliterate, for, however nearly they are assimilated in form or character, they never associate; and, when they meet, a combat generally ensues, which often terminates fatally to one of the parties.

RED TAILED HAWK   AMERICAN SPARROW HAWK

RED-TAILED HAWK.

FALCO BOREALIS.

Falco Borealis. Gmel. Syst. Nat. Vol. i. p. 266.—Latham. Ind. Ornith. Vol. i. p. 25. Arct. Zool. p. 205, No. 100. Ch. Buonaparte, Synops, p. 32. Wilson, Am. Orn. 2d ed. Vol. i. p. 82. *American Buzzard,* Lath. i. 50. Turt. Syst. p. 151. *F. aquilinus, cauda ferruginea, Great Eagle Hawk,* Bartram, p. 290. Philadelphia Museum.

The daring boldness of this Hawk is without parallel in its kind. Conscious of the superiority only of man, it seems, guided by instinct, to delay its depredations until the farmer is absent from his home, and then, with a rapid flight, it leaves its seat of observation, and silent as death, with wings motionless, it skims over the top of the orchard, direct for the farm house, appearing to choose this dense collection of foliage to hide it from view, until the first intimation of its approach is resounded from a hundred cackling throats, that the enemy is at hand, and the work of destruction done. By one swoop, scarcely retarded in its progress, this bird of prey seizes its victim in its powerful talons, and bears it off, still alive, and writhing in the agonies of death, to the wood.

The flight of this Hawk is regular and majestic when sailing in the air. In the autumn, when the cooling breezes of the north are playing through the faded leaves of the forests, then may be seen against a cloudless sky, the spiral movements of this bird. At first, it leaves its lofty seat with a few fluttering motions of the wings, and then with motionless and outstretched pinions, it cleaves the air, in a continual circular flight, ascending gradually at every revolution, until it is finally lost to human ken. But when in search of prey, the majesty of the bird is obscured by its predatory designs. Its sight, which is only surpassed by that of the eagle, is most wonderful. Passing rapidly over woods or fields, the slightest motion on the earth or in the grass, is detected by the keenness of its vision; then its progress is immediately retarded by alighting on a neighbouring tree, or making a contracted circular flight over the spot whence the motion proceeded, until the cause which arrested its attention is fully ascertained; and if there be a subject for its appetite, it seldom fails to secure it. When seated on a tree, this Hawk is grave and watchful; its penetrating eye pierces through the thickly matted grass, and with the most intense vigilance, directs its attention to the spot where the prey lies concealed, and by one bound, like lightning it descends to the earth, and with unerring aim, secures the hapless victim.

AMERICAN SPARROW HAWK.

FALCO SPARVERIUS.

[Female.]

Falco Sparverius. Linn. Syst. ed. 10, p. 90. Gmel. Syst. 1, p. 284. Ind. Orn. p. 42.—*Emerillon de St. Domingue,* Buff. 1, 291. Pl. enl. 465. Arct. Zool. 212.—*Little Falcon,* Lath. Syn. V. 1, p. 114, No. 94, ib. 95.—*Little Hawk,* Arct. Zool. 211, No. 110.—*Emerillon de Cayenne,* Buff. 1, 291. Pl. enl. No. 444.—*F. Dominicensis,* Gmel. Syst. 1, p. 285.—*Little Hawk,* Catesby, 1, p. 5.—*L'Emerillon de la Caroline,* Briss. Orn. 1, p. 386.—*Tinnunculus Sparverius,* Vieil Ois. de l'Am. Sept. p. 12, 13.—J. Doughty's Collection.

"The habits and manners of this bird are well known. It flies rather irregularly, occasionally suspending itself in the air, hovering over a particular spot for a minute or two, and then shooting off in another direction. It perches on the top of a dead tree, or pole in the middle of a field or meadow, and as it alights shuts its long wings so suddenly that they seem instantly to disappear; it sits here in an almost perpendicular position, sometimes for an hour at a time, frequently jerking its tail, and reconnoitering the ground below, in every direction, for mice, lizards, &c. It approaches the farm-house, particularly in the morning, skulking about the barn-yard for mice or young chickens. It frequently plunges into a thicket after small birds, as if by random; but always with a particular, and generally a fatal, aim. One day I observed a bird of this species perched on the highest top of a large poplar, on the skirts of the wood; and was in the act of raising the gun to my eye when he swept down with the rapidity of an arrow into a thicket of briars about thirty yards off, where I shot him dead; and on coming up found a small field sparrow quivering in his grasp. Both our aims had been taken in the same instant, and, unfortunately for him, both were fatal. It is particularly fond of watching along hedge-rows, and in orchards, where those small birds, usually resort. When grasshoppers are plenty, they form a considerable part of its food.

"The Blue Jays have a particular antipathy to this bird, and frequently insult it by following and imitating its notes so exactly as to deceive even those well acquainted with both. In return for all this abuse the Hawk contents himself with, now and then, feasting on the plumpest of his persecutors; who are therefore in perpetual dread of him; and yet, through some strange infatuation, or from fear that if they lose sight of him he may attack them unawares, the Sparrow Hawk no sooner appears than the alarm is given, and the whole posse of Jays follow."

CANADA PORCUPINE.

HYSTRIX PILOSUS.

Hystrix Pilosus Americanus, Catesby. Carol. app. p. 30. Richardson, *Faun. Am. bor.* 214. *Porcupine from Hudson's bay*, Edwards. *Cavia Hudsonius*, Klein, *Quad.* p. 51. *Hystrix Hudsonius*, Brisson, *Regn. an.* p. 148. *Hystrix dorsata.* Lin. *syst.* p. 57. *Canada Porcupine*, Forster, *Phil. Tran.* lxii. p. 374. Pennant, *Quad.* ii. p. 126.. Godman, ii. 160. *Bear Porcupine*, Harlan. 190. *Porcupine of North America*, Cozzens, *Ann. Lyceum, Nat. Hist.* i. 190. *Eretizon dorsatum*, F. Cuvier, *Mem. de Mus.* ix. p. 431.—Philadelphia Museum.

The common Porcupine, (*H. cristata*) although known from the earliest ages, has given rise to numberless fables; among which, that commonly received, is, that it possesses the power of ejecting its quills to a considerable distance when irritated or pursued; but although it has not this mode of defending itself, it is by no means a contemptible antagonist, as when attacked it will throw itself with great fierceness towards its opponent, and almost always sideways, and as it is on the sides that the spines are strongest it often inflicts wounds by means of them; its bite is also very severe, from the strength and size of its incisor teeth. The use of this armature has been the subject of inquiry among naturalists, and does not appear to be well understood; the most probable idea, however, is, that, like that of the Hedgehog, it is merely for defence, as, like that animal, it has the power of rolling itself into a ball, and thus presenting a phalanx of spears on every side, that renders the attacks of most animals perfectly fruitless; in fact, it has few enemies to dread except that universal destroyer—man.

The Canada Porcupine is a very unsightly and sluggish animal, and is not provided with the long quills so remarkable in the last mentioned species, its armature consisting of short sharp spines almost concealed by the hair with which they are intermingled. Buffon terms it *urson*, intending, as is observed by Dr. Richardson, to recall the memory of Hudson, the discoverer of the country where it abounds, and also to denote its spiny appearance, resembling that of the Hedgehog, (*herisson*). As will be seen by the list of synonymes, it has received a variety of appellations from different naturalists, and as Catesby's name of *pilosus* was bestowed upon it prior to that of *dorsata*, we have adopted it, though the other is generally retained by authors. The following description of it, by Dr. Richardson, is so full, that we extract it, instead of attempting to draw out another.

"*Form.*—Body thick and clumsy, back much arched in a regular curve from the nose to the buttocks, when it drops more rapidly to the tail, which is very low. *Legs* very short. *Tail*, short, thick, rounded at the tip, and turned a little upwards. *Nose* flattish above, broad and abrupt. There is a narrow, naked margin round the nostrils, but there is no smooth dividing line on the upper lip. *Eyes*, lateral, very small, and round. *Ears* situated behind and above the auditory opening, covered as thickly with fur as the neighouring parts, and entirely concealed by it. *Incisors* nearly as strong as those of the beaver. They curve forward a little so as to project beyond the nose, are convex anteriorly narrower behind, and are not much compressed. They have a yellow colour. The crowns of the grinders, as they wear, acquire an even surface."

"*Fur.*—The upper lip covered with short hair of a dull yellowish brown colour. The cheeks and forehead are clothed with liver brown hair, moderately long, interspersed with a very few black and white hairs. The hair on the body, both above and below, is long, and of a dull liver-brown colour, intermixed on all the upper parts, and on the hips with still larger hairs, some of which are entirely black, others entirely white, and a third set black at the roots and white at tip. The white hairs are most numerous on the posterior part of the body. There are also many round, spindle shaped, sharp pointed spines or quills, fixed among the hair which covers the upper parts. The spines commence on the crown of the head, and are there short, thick, very sharp pointed and very numerous. There are a good many longer and more slender ones on the shoulders and fore part of the back. There are also many on the sides and middle of the back, but these are still more slender and flexible, as well as less conspicuous. The buttocks and thighs are thickly set with long, very strong, and sharp spines. Some of these are entirely white, others brown at tip. The *throat* and *belly* are covered with brown hair, not so long as that on the back, lying more smoothly, and unmixed with either white hairs or spines. The *tail* is covered with brown hair above and below, and soiled white hair on its margin and tip. There are many small spines among the hair on its upper surface. "

The Canada Porcupine, however, varies much in colour; though the above is the most common, sometimes they have been found quite white, and at others of an almost universal dark brown. The spines or quills are attached but slightly to the skin, and from being barbed at tip with numerous small reversed points or prickles, they penetrate by degrees very deep into the flesh after having been once lodged. On the animal's being irritated, he has the power of directing their points in every direction, and small and insignificant as these weapons may appear, they are capable of causing the death of dogs, wolves, or indeed of any animal that incautiously attempts to seize the Porcupine. These quills are in great request among the aborigines, who use them in great quantities in the manufacture of a number of ornaments, previously dying them, in a very permanent manner, of variety of colours.

SUMMER DUCK

SUMMER DUCK, OR WOOD DUCK.

Le Canard d'Eté, Briss. vi. *p.* 351. 11. *pl. 32. fig. 2.—
Le beau Canard huppé*, Buff. ix, *p.* 245.—*Pl. Enl.*
980. 981.—*Summer Duck*, Catesby, i, *pl.* 97.—Edw.
pl. 101.—*Arct. Zool. No.* 943.—Lath. *Syn.* iii. *p.*
546.—*Anas sponsa*, Gmel. *Syst.* i, *p.* 539, *No.* 43.—
Ind. Orn. p. 876, *No.* 97.—Philadelphia Museum.

This most beautiful of all our Ducks, has probably no
superior among its whole tribe for richness and variety of
colours. It is called the *Wood Duck*, from the circumstance of its breeding in hollow trees; and the *Summer
Duck*, from remaining with us chiefly during the summer.
It is familiarly known in every quarter of the United States,
from Florida to Lake Ontario, in the neighbourhood of
which latter place I have myself met with it in October.
It rarely visits the seashore, or salt marshes; its favourite
haunts being the solitary deep and muddy creeks, ponds,
and mill dams of the interior, making its nest frequently in
old hollow trees that overhang the water.

The Summer Duck is equally well known in Mexico and
many of the West India islands. During the whole of our
winters they are occasionally seen in the States south of the
Potomac. On the tenth of January I met with two on a
creek near Petersburg in Virginia. In the more northern
districts, however, they are migratory. In Pennsylvania
the female usually begins to lay late in April or early in
May. Instances have been known where the nest was constructed of a few sticks laid in a fork of the branches; usually, however, the inside of a hollow tree is selected for
this purpose. On the eighteenth of May I visited a tree
containing the nest of a Summer Duck, on the banks of
Tuckahoe river, New Jersey. It was an old grotesque
white oak, whose top had been torn off by a storm. It
stood on the declivity of the bank, about twenty yards from
the water. In this hollow and broken top, and about six
feet down, on the soft decayed wood, lay thirteen eggs,
snugly covered with down, doubtless taken from the breast
of the bird. These eggs were of an exact oval shape, less
than those of a hen, the surface exceedingly fine grained,
and of the highest polish and slightly yellowish, greatly
resembling old polished ivory. The egg measured two
inches and an eighth by one inch and a half. On breaking
one of them, the young bird was found to be nearly hatched,
but dead, as neither of the parents had been observed about

the tree during the three or four days preceding; and were
conjectured to have been shot.

This tree had been occupied, probably by the same pair,
for four successive years, in breeding time; the person who
gave me the information, and whose house was within
twenty or thirty yards of the tree, said that he had seen the
female, the spring preceding, carry down thirteen young,
one by one, in less than ten minutes. She caught them in
her bill by the wing or back of the neck, and landed them
safely at the foot of the tree, whence she afterwards led
them to the water. Under this same tree, at the time I
visited it, a large sloop lay on the stocks, nearly finished,
the deck was not more than twelve feet distant from the
nest, yet notwithstanding the presence and noise of the
workmen, the ducks would not abandon their old breeding
place, but continued to pass out and in as if no person had
been near. The male usually perched on an adjoining limb,
and kept watch while the female was laying; and also often
while she was sitting. A tame goose had chosen a hollow
space at the root of the same tree, to lay and hatch her
young in.

The Summer Duck seldom flies in flocks of more than
three or four individuals together, and most commonly in
pairs, or singly. The common note of the drake is *peet,
peet;* but, when standing sentinel, he sees danger, he makes
a noise not unlike the crowing of a young cock, *oe eek!
oe eek!* Their food consists principally of acorns, chesnuts,
seeds of the wild oats, and insects. Their flesh is inferior
to that of the Blue-winged Teal. They are frequent in the
markets of Philadelphia and New York.

Among other gaudy feathers with which the Indians ornament the calumet, or pipe of peace, the skin of the head
and neck of the Summer Duck is frequently seen covering
the stem.

This beautiful bird has often been tamed, and soon becomes so familiar as to permit one to stroke its back with
the hand. I have seen individuals so tamed in various
parts of the Union. Captain Boyce, collector of the port
of Havre-de-Grace, informs me that about forty years ago,
a Mr. Nathan Nicols, who lived on the west side of Gun-
powder creek, had a whole yard swarming with Summer
Ducks, which he had tamed and completely domesticated,
so that they bred and were as familiar as any other tame
fowls; that he (Capt. Boyce) himself saw them in that state,
but does not know what became of them. Latham says
that they are often kept in European menageries, and will
breed there.

GREAT TAILED SQUIRREL

GREAT TAILED SQUIRREL.

SCIURUS MACROURUS.

Sciurus macrourus, SAY. *non* GMELIN, *S. magnicau-datus*, HARLAN. *Griffith, An. king. S. macroureus*, GODMAN. *Am. Nat. Hist.* Philadelphia Museum.

Few animals are to be compared to the Squirrels for beauty, and lightness of form, and grace and agility of movements. Living on the loftiest trees, they bound from limb to limb, with a rapidity that almost resembles flying. Few animals also, especially among the smaller classes, become so readily tamed, and submit with such apparent contentment, to the loss of liberty, and a confinement so widely different from their natural habits.

The true Squirrels of North America are by no means as large, nor is the colour of their fur as rich as those species inhabiting the eastern parts of Asia; with a few exceptions they are of an ash grey colour of various shades, and the specific peculiarities and markings by which they are distinguished, are so slight, that it is a task of no little difficulty to ascertain the number of species inhabiting our forests.

The subject of our present plate was first described by Mr. Say, in "Long's Expedition to the Rocky Mountains," from specimens found on the Missouri, where it is the most common species. This gentleman described it under the name of *macrourus*, without perhaps being aware that this appellation had already been given by Gmelin to the Ceylon Squirrel; from this latter circumstance Dr. Harlan changed the name to that of *magnicaudatus*, and Dr. Godman *macroureus;* as, however, Cuvier states that the Ceylon Squirrel is identical with the great Indian Squirrel, *S. maximus,* Mr. Say's original name can still be retained for this species.

When the animal is in its summer dress, the fur on the back is from three-fifths to seven-tenths of an inch in length; whilst in the winter coat, the longest hairs on the middle of the back are from one to one inch and three quarters long, the colours, however, do not vary. From this difference in the length of the fur, and the greater proportion of fat, the animal appears shorter and thicker than in summer.

The total length of this species, from the tip of the nose to the end of the tail, exclusive of the hair, is nineteen inches and three quarters, of which the tail makes nine inches and a tenth. The tail is much larger and finer than in the common Grey Squirrel, (*S. cinereus.*)

Mr. Say observes, "This species was not an unfrequent article of food at our frugal yet social meals at Engineer Cantonment, and we could always immediately distinguish the bones from those of other animals by their remarkable red colour."

RAVEN

RAVEN.

CORVUS CORAX.

Gmel. *Syst.* i, *p.* 364.—*Ind. Orn. p.* 150.—*Le Corbeau,* Briss. 2. *p.* 8, *et var.*—Buff. *Ois.* 3, *p.* 13. *Pl. enl.* 495.—Temm. *Man. d'Orn. p.* 107.—*Raven,* Lath. *Gen. Syn.* i. *p.* 367. *Id. sup. p.* 74.—Penn. *Brit. Zool. No.* 74. *Arct. Zool. No.* 134.—Shaw, *Gen. Zool.* 7, *p.* 341.—Bewick, 1, *p.* 100.—Low, *Fauna Orcadensis, p.* 45.—Philada. *Museum.*

A knowledge of this celebrated bird has been handed down to us from the earliest ages; and its history is almost coeval with that of man. In the best and most ancient of all books, we learn, that at the end of forty days, after the great flood had covered the earth, Noah, wishing to ascertain whether or not the waters had abated, sent forth a Raven, which did not return into the ark.* This is the first notice that is taken of this species. Though the Raven was declared unclean by the law of Moses, yet we are informed, that when the prophet Elijah provoked the enmity of Ahab, by prophesying against him; and hid himself by the brook Cherith, the Ravens were appointed by Heaven to bring him his daily food.† The colour of the Raven gave rise to a similitude in one of the most beautiful of eclogues, which has been perpetuated in all subsequent ages, and which is not less pleasing for being trite or proverbial. The favourite of the royal lover of Jerusalem, in the enthusiasm of affection, thus describes the object of her adoration, in reply to the following question:

'What is thy beloved more than another beloved, O thou fairest among women?' 'My beloved is white and ruddy, the chiefest among ten thousand. His head is as the most fine gold, *his locks are bushy, and black as a Raven.*'‡

The above mentioned circumstances taken into consideration, one should suppose that the lot of the subject of this chapter would have been of a different complexion from what history and tradition inform us is the fact. But in every country, we are told, the Raven is considered an ominous bird, whose croakings foretell approaching evil; and many a crooked beldam has given interpretation to these oracles, of a nature to infuse terror into a whole community. Hence this ill-fated bird, immemorially, has been the innocent subject of vulgar detestation.

* Gen. viii. 7.　　　† 1 Kings, xvii. 5, 6.
‡ Song of Solomon, v. 9, 10, 11.

Augury, or the art of foretelling future events by the flight, cries, or motion of birds, descended from the Chaldeans to the Greeks, thence to the Etrurians, and from them it was transmitted to the Romans.* The crafty legislators of these celebrated nations, from a deep knowledge of human nature, made superstition a principal feature of their religious ceremonies; well knowing that it required a more than ordinary policy to govern a multitude, ever liable to the fatal influences of passion; and who, without some timely restraints, would burst forth like a torrent, whose course is marked by wide-spreading desolation. Hence, to the purposes of polity the Raven was made subservient; and the Romans having consecrated it to Apollo, as to the god of divination, its flight was observed with the greatest solemnity; and its tones and inflections of voice were noted with a precision, which intimated a belief in its infallible prescience.

But the ancients have not been the only people infected with this species of superstition: the moderns, even though favoured with the light of Christianity, have exhibited as much folly, through the impious curiosity of prying into futurity, as the Romans themselves. It is true that modern nations have not instituted their sacred colleges or sacerdotal orders, for the purposes of divination; but in all countries there have been self-constituted augurs, whose interpretations of omens have been received with religious respect by the credulous multitude. Even at this moment, in some parts of the world, if a Raven alight on a village church, the whole fraternity is in an uproar; and Heaven is importuned, in all the ardour of devotion, to avert the impending calamity.

The poets have taken advantage of this weakness of human nature, and in their hands the Raven is a fit instrument of terror. Shakspeare puts the following malediction into the mouth of his Caliban:

"As wicked dew as ere my mother brush'd
With *Raven's* feather, from unwholesome fen
Drop on you both!"†

* That the science of augury is very ancient, we learn from the Hebrew lawgiver, who prohibits it, as well as every other kind of divination. Deut. chap. xviii. The Romans derived their knowledge of augury chiefly from the Tuscans or Etrurians, who practised it in the earliest times. This art was known in Italy before the time of Romulus, since that prince did not commence the building of Rome till he had taken the auguries. The successors of Romulus, from a conviction of the usefulness of the science, and at the same time not to render it contemptible, by becoming too familiar, employed the most skilful augurs from Etruria, to introduce the practice of it into their religious ceremonies. And by a decree of the senate, some of the youth of the best families in Rome were annually sent into Tuscany, to be instructed in this art. Vide Ciceron. de Divin. Also Calmet, and the abbé Banier.

† Tempest, act i. scene 2.

The ferocious wife of Macbeth, on being advised of the approach of Duncan, whose death she had conspired, thus exclaims:

> "The *Raven* himself is hoarse,
> That croaks the fatal entrance of Duncan
> Under my battlements!"*

The Moor of Venice says:

> "It comes o'er my memory,
> As doth the *Raven* o'er the infected house,
> Boding to all."†

The last quotation alludes to the supposed habits of this bird flying over those houses which contain the sick, whose dissolution is at hand, and thereby announced. Thus Marlowe, in the Jew of Malta, as cited by Malone:

> "The sad presaging *Raven* tolls
> The sick man's passport in her hollow beak,
> And in the shadow of silent night
> Doth shake contagion from her sable wing."

But it is the province of philosophy to dispel those illusions which bewilder the mind, by pointing out the simple truths which Nature has been at no pains to conceal, but which the folly of mankind has shrouded in all the obscurity of mystery.

The Raven is a bird found in every region of the world; strong and hardy, he is uninfluenced by the change of the weather; and when other birds seem numbed with cold, or pining with famine, the Raven is active and healthy, busily employed in prowling for prey, or sporting in the coldest atmosphere. As the heats of the line do not oppress him, so he bears the cold of the polar countries with equal indifference. He is sometimes, indeed, seen milk-white, and this may probably be the effect of the rigorous climates of the north.

When the Raven is taken as a domestic, he has many qualities that renders him extremely amusing. Busy, inquisitive, and impudent, he goes every where, affronts and drives off the dogs, plays his pranks on the poultry, and is particularly assiduous in cultivating the goodwill of the cook maid, who seems to be the favourite of the family. But then, with the amusing qualities of a favourite, he often also has the vices and defects. He is a glutton by nature, and a thief by habit. He does not confine himself to petty depredations on the pantry or the larder; he soars at more magnificent plunder; at spoils which he can neither exhibit nor enjoy; but which, like a miser, he rests satisfied with having the satisfaction of sometimes visiting and contemplating in secret. A piece of money, a tea-spoon, or a ring, are always tempting baits to his avarice; these he will slily seize upon, and, if not watched, will carry to his favourite hole.

In his wild state, the Raven is an active and greedy plunderer. Nothing comes amiss to him. If in his flights he perceives no hope of carrion, (and his scent is so exquisite, that he can smell it at a vast distance), he then contents himself with more unsavoury food, fruits, insects, and the accidental deserts of a dunghill. This bird chiefly builds its nest in trees, and lays five or six eggs of a pale green colour, marked with small brownish spots.

---

* Act i. scene 5.   † Othello, act iv. scene 1.

THE CABINET

OF

NATURAL HISTORY

AND

American Rural Sports

WITH

Illustrations.

VOLUME II.

T. Doughty del.   W. E. Tucker sc.

—1832.—

PHILADELPHIA

Published by J & T Doughty

Will. Bartram

Engraved by T.B.Welch from an Original Painting by C.W.Peale.

BIOGRAPHICAL SKETCH

OF

WILLIAM BARTRAM.

In a short biographical notice, like the present must necessarily be, little more can be said of a man, than to give the general outlines of character and the leading incidents of his life.

Of Mr. Bartram, the world, in times past, knew much, for his fame extended to both continents; in his sphere, he was one of the most eminent men of America; his knowledge was acquired by incessant mental and bodily labour; the fields of natural science in his early days were unexplored, and he resorted to the study of nature where she unfolds her works to the senses as the only true source of knowledge, and it seems due to his eminence, to offer a small tribute of respect in a biographical way, that his example for temperance, application to the study of science, perseverance, and the strict performance of his social duties, should be given for the benefit and encouragement of others.

The accompanying portrait is a correct likeness of Mr. Bartram, and the only engraved one ever given to the American public.

JOHN BARTRAM, (father to the subject of the present biography,) was a celebrated and self-taught philosopher and botanist, and was born near the village of Darby, in Delaware county, Pennsylvania, in the year 1701. His grandfather, John Bartram, and family, emigrated to Pennsylvania from Derbyshire, in England, with some of the adherents of William Penn, in 1682. In very early life he manifested much desire for knowledge, but the means of education at that period in the colonies were not sufficient to satisfy his thirst for knowledge, and being at so great a distance from Europe, he had to content himself with only a moderate education, and rely on the resources of his own mind, and apply himself to books and the society of literary and eminent men; the result was, that he acquired a knowledge of other languages, and it is said, that " so earnest was he in the pursuit of learning, that he seldom sat at his meals without his book; often his victuals in one hand and his book in the other," and by

such indefatigable application he soon fitted himself for the highest scale of society; he was bred a husbandman, and while cultivating the grounds as means to support his family, he prosecuted his avocations as a philosopher. The vegetable kingdom, however, attracted most his attention, and he applied himself with renewed vigour to the study of botany.

He was the first American who conceived and executed the design of a botanic garden; this he located in a delightful situation on the banks of the Schuylkill river, about four miles from Philadelphia, on a spot which embraced a variety of soils and situations to the extent of six or seven acres, and enriched it with a great variety of indigenous and exotic plants; many of the former having been collected by himself during his travels in various parts from Canada to Florida. His progress in philosophy, botany, and other branches of natural history, attracted the notice and esteem of the principal literary and eminent characters of America, and the correspondence and friendship of many of those of Europe; in consequence of which he was frequently employed in collecting what was new and curious to furnish and ornament many of the European gardens with the productions of the new world, and he was at last appointed American Botanist to George the Third, in which appointment he continued until his death, in September, 1777, in the 76th year of his age.

He left several children. John, (the fifth son,) succeeded him as proprietor of the Kingsess botanic garden, which, after his death, in 1812, was inherited by his daughter, Mrs. Carr, wife of Col. Robert Carr, in whose possession it still remains.

WILLIAM BARTRAM, known as a traveller and a botanist, was the fourth son of John Bartram, and was born April the 9th, 1739, at the botanic garden, Kingsessing township, near Philadelphia.

His education was a moderate one, and nothing remarkable appeared in his character during the early part of his youth, which was chiefly spent in agricultural pursuits; this, however, he soon relinquished to serve an apprenticeship to a respectable merchant of Philadelphia, and at the age of 22 he went to Wilmington, N. C., with the view of entering into the mercantile business, but being ardently attached to the study of botany, he left that place in about four years, and accompanied his father on a journey into East Florida, to explore the natural production of that country; and it was during this period he discovered the Franklinia, a beautiful tree, so called in honour of Dr. Franklin. After this he settled on the River St. Johns, in the same territory, and commenced the cultivation of indigo, but soon abandoned it in consequence of bad health, and returned in the year 1771 to his father's residence.

The information acquired by his travels and researches now began to bring him to the notice of the eminent and learned men of both America and England, and at the solicitations and expense of Dr. Fothergill, of London, he made excursions to the Floridas and the western parts of Carolina and Georgia, in search of rare and useful productions of nature, but chiefly of the vegetable kingdom, to which gentleman he sent his collection of plants, dried specimens, and drawings.

From a diary kept by him during these travels he was enabled to furnish the world with a large volume of the most interesting and useful information, chiefly relating to the comparatively unexplored parts of those inhospitable regions, through which, at that early period, the traveller seldom bent his way merely for the love of science and the studies of nature.

This work was published in three countries about the year 1791 to 1793, viz: in Germany, Ireland, (Dublin,) and the United States, in an octavo form of upwards of 500 pages.

Mr. Bartram set sail on his intended journey from Philadelphia in April, 1773, in the brig Charleston Packet, for Charleston, where he arrived after a very tedious and stormy passage of eleven days from the Capes; here he remained a few days, and gained the friendship of many of the most wealthy and respectable families, when he departed for Savannah on his intended expedition.

At this period Georgia and the Floridas were inhabited, and, indeed, overrun with different tribes of Indians; many of whom were exceedingly hostile to the whites— from this circumstance, as well as the nature of the country, the miserable roads, and other difficulties in travelling, it became extremely unpleasant, and, at times, hazardous for Mr. Bartram to prosecute his journey; but his experience had prepared him for hardships, and, being of a humane and amiable disposition, he went forward in the confidence that others felt toward him, as he felt toward all mankind—while these benevolent feelings were frequently manifested in his countenance and demeanour, and on several occasions worked safety for him when extreme danger was at hand.(1)

In all his travels, Mr. Bartram singularly adhered to the

(1) I arrived at St. Ille's in the evening, where I lodged; and next morning, having crossed over in a ferry-boat, set forward for St. Mary's. The situation of the territory, its soil and productions, between these two last rivers, are nearly similar to those which I had passed over, exept that the savannahs are more frequent and extensive.

It may be proper to observe, that I had now passed the utmost frontier of the white settlements on that border. It was drawing on towards the close of day, the skies serene and calm, the air temperately cool, and gentle zephyrs breathing through the fragrant pine; the prospect around enchantingly varied and beautiful; endless green savannahs, chequered with coppices of fragrant shrubs, filled the air with the richest perfume. The gaily attired plants which enamelled the green had begun to imbibe the pearly dew of evening; nature seemed silent, and nothing appeared to ruffle the happy moments of evening contemplation; when, on a sudden, an Indian appeared crossing the path, at a considerable distance before me. On perceiving that he was armed with a rifle, the first sight of him startled me, and I endeavoured to elude his sight, by stopping my pace, and keeping large trees between us; but he espied me, and turning short about, set spurs to his horse, and came up on full gallop. I never before this was afraid at the sight of an Indian, but at this time, I must own that my spirits were much agitated: I saw at once, that being unarmed, I was in his power; and having now but a few moments to prepare, I resigned myself entirely to the will of the Almighty, trusting to his mercies for my preservation: my mind then became tranquil, and I resolved to meet the dreaded foe with resolution and cheerful confidence. The in-

trepid Siminole stopped suddenly, three or four yards before me, and silently viewed me, his countenance angry and fierce, shifting his rifle from shoulder to shoulder, and looking about instantly on all sides. I advanced towards him, and with an air of confidence offered him my hand, hailing him, brother; at this he hastily jerked back his arm, with a look of malice, rage, and disdain, seeming every way discontented; when again looking at me more attentively, he instantly spurred up to me, and with dignity in his look and action, gave me his hand. Possibly the silent language of his soul, during the moment of suspense, (for I believe his design was to kill me when he first came up,) was after this manner: " White man, thou art my enemy, and thou and thy brethren may have killed mine; yet it may not be so, and even were that the case, thou art now alone, and in my power. Live; the great Spirit forbids me to touch thy life; go to thy brethren, tell them thou sawest an Indian in the forests, who knew how to be humane and compassionate." In fine, we shook hands, and parted in a friendly manner, in the midst of a dreary wilderness; and he informed me of the course and distance to the trading-house, where I found he had been extremely ill treated the day before.

I now sat forward again, and after eight or ten miles riding, arrived at the banks of St. Mary's, opposite the stores, and got safe over before dark. The river is here about one hundred yards across, has ten feet water, and, following its course, about sixty miles to the sea, though but about twenty miles by land. The trading company here received and treated me with great civility. On relating my adventures on the road, particularly the last with the Indian, the chief re-

objects of his search, not only in noticing the more common, but scrutinizing every plant which appeared new to him, or would be rare to others interested in the botanical kingdom. His researches, as before stated, attracted the notice of some of the chief men of London, among whom was Sir Joseph Banks, President of the Royal Society; this nobleman, (whether for himself or the Society over which he presided, is not precisely known,) wishing to avail himself of the services of our traveller, offered him *one shilling sterling* for every new plant which he might discover in these southern districts, which offer drew the following laconic answer:

" William Bartram, in answer to Joseph Banks' proposal, says, that there are not over five hundred species of plants altogether in the provinces of Virginia, North Carolina, South Carolina, West and East Florida, and Georgia, which, at one shilling each, amounts only to £25—supposing every thing acceptable. It has taken him two years to search only part of the two last provinces, and finds by experience it cannot be done with tolerable conveniency for less than £100 a year, therefore it cannot reasonably be expected that he can accept the offer."

Mr. Bartram was occupied five years in these researches, during which period he discovered a large number of new plants, and contributed most extensive information relative to the natural history of the country; he was the first American ornithologist, and his table of birds was regarded as the only correct list extant, in which two hundred and fifteen different species are enumerated; this table is to be found in his work, page 285, of the Dublin edition.

After his return home, he devoted himself still more closely to science; and in April, 1782, he was elected Professor of Botany in the University of Pennsylvania, but declined serving in consequence of the impaired state of his health; he was also elected a member of several other scientific institutions in the city of Philadelphia.

In 1776, just at the commencement of the Revolutionary War, and while on his return from Florida to Georgia, Mr. Bartram volunteered and joined a detachment of men, raised by Gen. Lochlan McIntosh, to repel a supposed invasion of that state from St. Augustine by the British; he was offered a lieutenant's commission if he would remain, but the report which led him to volunteer his services having proved false, the detachment was disbanded, and Mr. Bartram resumed his travels. Mr. Bartram possessed a full share of republican principles, which were imbibed at a very early age, the first impressions being given when at school by his tutor, Charles Thomson, afterwards Secretary to Congress during the revolution; and Mr. Bartram was frequently heard to say, how careful Mr. Thomson was, on every possible occasion, to instil republican principles into the minds of his youthful pupils.

As a writer, Mr. Bartram, at times, was graphic, and generally delineated things as he saw them, although here and there some extravagant or enthusiastic remarks accompany his descriptions, yet, upon the whole, he was easy, intelligent, and instructive; he was often placed in unpleasant and sometimes perilous circumstances during his travels; and his account of the alligators and frequent encounters with them, cannot be read without the most thrilling interest.(2) Indeed, so powerful were the impres-

---

plied, with a countenance that at once bespoke surprise and pleasure, " My friend, consider yourself a fortunate man: ' that fellow,' said he, ' is one of the greatest villains on earth, a noted murderer, and outlawed by his countrymen. Last evening he was here, we took his gun from him, broke it in pieces, and gave him a severe drubbing; he, however, made his escape, carrying off a new rifle gun, with which, he said, going off, he would kill the first white man he met.' "

On seriously contemplating the behaviour of this Indian towards me, so soon after his ill treatment, the following train of sentiments insensibly crowded in upon my mind:

Can it be denied, but that the moral principle, which directs the savages to virtuous and praiseworthy actions, is natural or innate? It is certain they have not the assistance of letters, or those means of education in the schools of philosophy, where the virtuous sentiments and actions of the most illustrious characters are recorded, and carefully laid before the youth of civilized nations: therefore this moral principle must be innate, or they must be under the immediate influence and guidance of a more divine and powerful preceptor, who, on these occasions, instantly inspires them, and, as with a ray of divine light, points out to them at once the dignity, propriety, and beauty of virtue.

(2) The evening was temperately cool and calm. The crocodiles began to roar and appear in uncommon numbers along the shores and in the river. I fixed my camp in an open plain, near the utmost projection of the promontory, under the shelter of a large live oak, which stood on the highest part of the ground, and but a few yards from my boat. From this open, high situation, I had a free prospect of the river, which was a matter of no trivial consideration to me, having good reason to dread the subtle attacks of the alligators, who were crowding about my harbour. Having collected a good quantity of wood for the purpose of keeping up a light and smoke during the night, I began to think of preparing my supper, when, upon examining my stores, I found but a scanty provision. I thereupon determined, as the most expeditious way of supplying my necessities, to take my bob and try for some trout. About one hundred yards above my harbour began a cove or bay of the river, out of which opened a large lagoon. The mouth or entrance from the river to it was narrow, but the waters soon afterwards spread and formed a little lake, extending into the marshes: its entrance and shores within I observed to be verged with floating lawns of the pistia and nymphea, and other aquatic plants; these I knew were excellent haunts for trout.

sions left on Mr. Bartram by these unpleasant occurrences, that he never could entirely divest himself of them, and years after they had passed, he was heard to say, that he was often startled from his sleep by violent and hideous dreams of his encounters with these monsters.

The difficulties under which the lamented Wilson laboured, in the commencement and progress of his work, were, at times, almost insurmountable, and had nigh terminated his labours in the cause of ornithology; but in Mr. Bartram he found a friend, an undeviating friend, on whose counsel and guidance he always relied with filial

The verges and islets of the lagoon were elegantly embellished with flowering plants and shrubs; the laughing coots with wings half spread were tripping over the little coves and hiding themselves in the tufts of grass; young broods of the painted summer teal, skimming the still surface of the waters, and following the watchful parent unconscious of danger, were frequently surprised by the voracious trout; and he, in turn, as often by the subtle greedy alligator. Behold him rushing forth from the flags and reeds. His enormous body swells. His plaited tail brandished high, floats upon the lake. The waters like a cataract descend from his opening jaws. Clouds of smoke issue from his dilated nostrils. The earth trembles with his thunder. When immediately from the opposite coast of the lagoon, emerges from the deep his rival champion. They suddenly dart upon each other. The boiling surface of the lake marks their rapid course, and a terrific conflict commences. They now sink to the bottom folded together in horrid wreathes. The water becomes thick and discoloured. Again they rise, their jaws clap together, re-echoing through the deep surrounding forests. Again they sink, when the contest ends at the muddy bottom of the lake, and the vanquished makes a hazardous escape, hiding himself in the muddy turbulent waters and sedge on a distant shore. The proud victor exulting returns to the place of action. The shores and forests resound his dreadful roar, together with the triumphing shouts of these plaited tribes around, witnesses of the horrid combat.

My apprehensions were highly alarmed after being a spectator of so dreadful a battle. It was obvious that every delay would but tend to increase my dangers and difficulties, as the sun was near setting, and the alligators gathered around my harbour from all quarters. From these considerations I concluded to be expeditious in my trip to the lagoon, in order to take some fish. Not thinking it prudent to take my fusee with me, lest I might lose it overboard in case of a battle, which I had every reason to dread before my return, I therefore furnished myself with a club for my defence, went on board, and penetrating the first line of those which surrounded my harbour, they gave way; but being pursued by several very large ones, I kept strictly on the watch, and paddled with all my might towards the entrance of the lagoon, hoping to be sheltered there from the multitude of my assailants; but ere I had half way reached the place, I was attacked on all sides, several endeavouring to overset the canoe. My situation now became precarious to the last degree: two very large ones attacked me closely, at the same instant, rushing up with their heads and part of their bodies above the water, roaring terribly and belching floods of water over me. They struck their jaws together so close to my ears, as almost to stun me, and I expected every moment to be dragged out of the boat and instantly devoured. But I applied my weapons so effectually about me, though at random, that I was so successful as to beat them off a little; when, finding that they designed to renew the battle, I made for the shore, as the only means left me for my preservation; for, by keeping close to it, I should have my enemies on one side only, whereas I was before surrounded by them; and there was a probability, if pushed to the last extremity, of saving myself, by jumping out of the canoe on shore, as it is easy to outwalk them on land, although comparatively as swift as lightning in the water. I found this last expedient alone could fully answer my expectations, for as soon as I gained the shore, they drew off and kept aloof. This was a happy relief, as my confidence was, in some degree, recovered by it. On recollecting myself, I discovered that I had almost reached the entrance of the lagoon, and determined to veture in, if possible, to take a few fish, and then return to my harbour, while day-light continued; for I could now, with caution and resolution, make my way with safety along shore; and, indeed, there was no other way to regain my camp, without leaving my boat and making my retreat through the marshes and reeds, which, if I could even effect, would have been in a manner throwing myself away, for then there would have been no hopes of ever recovering my bark, and returning in safety to any settlements of men. I accordingly proceeded, and made good my entrance into the lagoon, though not without opposition from the alligators, who formed a line across the entrance, but did not pursue me into it, nor was I molested by any there, though there were some very large ones in a cove at the upper end. I soon caught more trout than I had present occasion for, and the air was too hot and sultry to admit of their being kept for many hours, even though salted or barbecued. I now prepared for my return to camp, which I succeeded in with but little trouble, by keeping close to the shore; yet I was opposed upon re-entering the river out of the lagoon, and pursued near to my landing, (though not closely attacked,) particularly by an old daring one, about twelve feet in length, who kept close after me; and when I stepped on shore, and turned about, in order to draw up my canoe, he rushed up near my feet, and lay there for some time, looking me in the face, his head and shoulders out of water. I resolved he should pay for his temerity, and having a heavy load in my fusee, I ran to my camp, and returning with my piece, found him with his foot on the gunwale of the boat, in search of fish. On my coming up he withdrew sullenly and slowly into the water, but soon returned and placed himself in his former position, looking at me, and seeming neither fearful nor any way disturbed. I soon despatched him by lodging the contents of my gun in his head, and then proceeded to cleanse and prepare my fish for supper; and accordingly took them out of the boat, laid them down on the sand close to the water, and began to scale them; when, raising my head, I saw before me, through the clear water, the head and shoulders of a very large alligator, moving slowly towards me. I instantly stepped back, when, with a sweep of his tail, he brushed off several of my fish. It was certainly most providential that I looked up at that instant, as the monster would, probably, in less than a minute, have seized and dragged me into the river. This incredible boldness of the animal disturbed me greatly, supposing there could now be no reasonable safety for me during the night, but by keeping continually on the watch: I therefore, as soon as I had prepared the fish, proceeded to secure myself and effects in the best manner I could. In the first place, I hauled my bark upon the shore, almost clear out of the water, to prevent their oversetting or sinking her; after this, every movable was taken out and carried to my camp, which was but a few yards off; then ranging some dry wood in such order as was the most convenient, I cleared the ground round about it, that there might be no impediment in my way, in case of an attack

piety. It was through the encouragement and assistance rendered by Mr. Bartram, that Wilson commenced and completed his splendid work on ornithology; and by his constant visits to the rural and delightful grounds of the botanic garden, he first conceived the plan of forming the work; he there also became enamoured of the study, and acquainted with a large number of birds figured in his work; how often in his writings does he allude to his friend, William Bartram, and this enchanting spot, so congenial with his feelings! In a letter to Mr. Bartram on the subject, Wilson says:

"I send you a few more imitations of birds for your opinion

in the night, either from the water or the land; for I discovered by this time, that this small isthmus, from its remote situation and fruitfulness, was resorted to by bears and wolves. Having prepared myself in the best manner I could, I charged my gun and proceeded to reconnoitre my camp and the adjacent grounds; when I discovered that the peninsula and grove, at the distance of about two hundred yards from my encampment, on the land side, were invested by a cypress swamp, covered with water, which below was joined to the shore of the little lake, and above to the marshes surrounding the lagoon; so that I was confined to an islet exceedingly circumscribed, and I found there was no other retreat for me, in case of an attack, but by either ascending one of the large oaks, or pushing off with my boat.

It was by this time dusk, and the alligators had nearly ceased their roar, when I was again alarmed by a tumultuous noise that seemed to be in my harbour, and therefore engaged my immediate attention. Returning to my camp I found it undisturbed, and then continued on to the extreme point of the promontory, where I saw a scene, new and surprising, which at first threw my senses into such a tumult, that it was some time before I could comprehend what was the matter; however, I soon accounted for the prodigious assemblage of crocodiles at this place, which exceeded every thing of the kind I had ever heard of.

How shall I express myself so as to convey an adequate idea of it to the reader, and at the same time avoid raising suspicions of my veracity! Should I say, that the river (in this place) from shore to shore, and perhaps near half a mile above and below me, appeared to be one solid bank of fish, of various kinds, pushing through this narrow pass of St. Juan's into the little lake, on their return down the river, and that the alligators were in such incredible numbers, and so close together from shore to shore, that it would have been easy to have walked across on their heads, had the animals been harmless? What expressions can sufficiently declare the shocking scene that for some minutes continued, whilst this mighty army of fish were forcing the pass? During this attempt, thousands, I may say hundreds of thousands of them were caught and swallowed by the devouring alligators. I have seen an alligator take up out of the water several great fish at a time, and just squeeze them betwixt his jaws, while the tails of the great trout flapped about his eyes and lips, ere he had swallowed them. The horrid noise of their closing jaws, their plunging amidst the broken banks of fish, and rising with their prey some feet upright above the water, the floods of water and blood rushing out of their mouths, and the clouds of vapour issuing from their wide nostrils, were truly frightful. This scene continued at intervals during the night, as the fish came to the pass. After this fight, shocking and tremendous as it was, I found myself somewhat easier and more reconciled to my situation; being convinced that their extraordinary assemblage here was owing to this annual feast of fish; and that they were so well employed in their own element, that I had little occasion to fear their paying me a visit.

It being now almost night, I returned to my camp, where I had left my fish broiling, and my kettle of rice stewing; and having with me oil, pepper and salt, and excellent oranges hanging in abundance over my head, (a valuable substitute for vinegar,) I sat down and regaled myself cheerfully. Having finished my repast, I rekindled my fire for light, and whilst I was revising the notes of my past day's journey, I was suddenly roused with a noise behind me toward the main land. I sprang up on my feet, and listening, I distinctly heard some creature wading in the water of the isthmus. I seized my gun, and went cautiously from my camp, directing my steps towards the noise: when I had advanced about thirty yards, I halted behind a coppice of orange trees, and soon perceived two very large bears, which had made their way through the water, and had landed in the grove, about one hundred yards distance from me, and were advancing towards me. I waited until they were within thirty yards of me: they there began to snuff and look towards my camp: I snapped my piece, but it flashed, on which they both turned about and galloped off, plunging through the water and swamp, never halting, as I suppose, until they reached fast land, as I could hear them leaping and plunging a long time. They did not presume to return again, nor was I molested by any other creature, except being occasionally awakened by the whooping of owls, screaming of bitterns, or the wood-rats running amongst the leaves.

The noise of the crocodiles kept me awake the greater part of the night; but when I arose in the morning, contrary to my expectations there was perfect peace; very few of them to be seen, and those were asleep on the shore. Yet I was not able to suppress my fears and apprehensions of being attacked by them in future; and, indeed, yesterday's combat with them, notwithstanding I came off in a manner victorious, or at least made a safe retreat, had left sufficient impression on my mind to damp my courage; and it seemed too much for one of my strength, being alone in a very small boat, to encounter such collected danger. To pursue my voyage up the river, and be obliged every evening to pass such dangerous defiles, appeared to me as perilous as running the gauntlet betwixt two rows of Indians armed with knives and firebrands. I however resolved to continue my voyage one day longer, if I possibly could with safety, and then return down the river, should I find the like difficulties to oppose. Accordingly I got every thing on board, charged my gun, and set sail cautiously, along shore. As I passed by Battle lagoon, I began to tremble and keep a good look out; when suddenly a huge alligator rushed out of the reeds, and with a tremendous roar came up, and darted as swift as an arrow under my boat, emerging upright on my lee quarter, with open jaws, and belching water and smoke that fell upon me like rain in a hurricane. I laid soundly about his head with my club and beat him off; and after plunging and darting about my boat, he went off on a straight line through the water, seemingly with the rapidity of lightning, and entered the cape of the lagoon. I now employed my time to the very best advantage in paddling close along shore, but could not forbear looking now and then behind me, and presently perceived one of them coming up again. The water of the river hereabouts was shoal and very clear: the monster came up with the usual roar and menaces, and passed close by the side of my boat, when I could distinctly see a young brood of alligators, to the number of one hundred or more, following after her in a long train. They kept close together in a

and correction, which I value beyond those of any body else, although I am seriously apprehensive that I am troublesome; these are the last I shall draw for some time, as it consumes every leisure moment I have, leaving nothing for friendship or the rural recreations I so much delight in."

On another occasion the same writer again addresses Mr. Bartram:

"The receipt of yours, of the 11th inst., (April, 1807,) in which you approve of my intended publication of American Ornithology, gave me much satisfaction; and your promise of befriending me in the arduous attempt commands my unfeigned gratitude. From the opportunities I have lately had of examining into the works of Americans who have treated of this part of our natural history, I am satisfied that none of them have bestowed such minute attention on the subject as you yourself have done. Indeed, they have done little more than copied your no-

column without straggling off to the one side or the other; the young appeared to be of an equal size, about fifteen inches in length, almost black, with pale yellow transverse waved clouds or blotches, much like rattlesnakes in colour. I now lost sight of my enemy again.

Still keeping close along shore, on turning a point or projection of the river bank, at once I beheld a great number of hillocks or small pyramids, resembling hay-cocks, ranged like an encampment along the banks. They stood fifteen or twenty yards distant from the water, on a high marsh, about four feet perpendicular above the water. I knew them to be the nests of the crocodile, having had a description of them before; and now expected a furious and general attack, as I saw several large crocodiles swimming abreast of these buildings. These nests being so great a curiosity to me, I was determined at all events immediately to land and examine them. Accordingly, I ran my bark on shore at one of their landing-places, which was a sort of nick or little dock, from which ascended a sloping path or road up to the edge of the meadow, where their nests were; most of them were deserted, and the great thick whitish egg-shells lay broken and scattered upon the ground round about them.

The nests or hillocks are of the form of an obtuse cone, four feet high and four or five feet in diameter at their bases; they are constructed with mud, grass, and herbage. At first they lay a floor of this kind of tempered mortar on the ground, upon which they deposit a layer of eggs, and upon this a stratum of mortar, seven or eight inches in thickness, and then another layer of eggs, and in this manner one stratum upon another, nearly to the top. I believe they commonly lay from one to two hundred eggs in a nest: these are hatched, I suppose, by the heat of the sun; and perhaps the vegetable substances mixed with the earth, being acted upon by the sun, may cause a small degree of fermentation, and so increase the heat in those hillocks. The ground for several acres about these nests showed evident marks of a continual resort of alligators; the grass was every where beaten down, hardly a blade or straw was left standing; whereas, all about, at a distance, it was five or six feet high, and as thick as it could grow together. The female, as I imagine, carefully watches her own nest of eggs until they are all hatched; or perhaps while she is attending her own brood, she takes under her care and protection as many as she can get at one time, either from her own particular nest or others; but certain it is, that the young are not left to shift for themselves; for I have had frequent opportunities of seeing the female alligator leading about the shores her train of young ones, just as a hen does her brood of chickens; and she is equally assiduous and courageous in defending the young, which are under her care, and providing for their subsistence; and when she is basking upon the warm banks, with her brood around her, you may hear the young ones continually whining and barking, like young puppies. I believe but few of a brood live to the years of full growth and magnitude, as the old feed on the young as long as they can make prey of them.

The alligator, when full grown, is a very large and terrible creature, and of prodigious strength, activity, and swiftness in the water. I have seen them twenty feet in length, and some are supposed to be twenty-two or twenty-three feet. Their body is as large as that of a horse; their shape exactly resembles that of a lizard, except their tail, which is flat or cuneiform, being compressed on each side, and gradually diminishing from the abdomen to the extremity, which, with the whole body, is covered with horny plates or squammæ, impenetrable when on the body of the live animal, even to a rifle-ball, except about their head and just behind their fore legs or arms, where, it is said, they are only vulnerable. The head of a full-grown one is about three feet, and the mouth opens nearly the same length; their eyes are small in proportion, and seem sunk deep in the head, by means of the prominency of the brows; the nostrils are large, inflated and prominent on the top, so that the head in the water resembles, at a distance, a great chunk of wood floating about. Only the upper jaw moves, which they raise almost perpendicular, so as to form a right angle with the lower one. In the fore-part of the upper jaw, on each side, just under the nostrils, are two very large, thick, strong teeth or tusks, not very sharp, but rather the shape of a cone: these are as white as the finest polished ivory, and are not covered by any skin or lips, and always in sight, which gives the creature a frightful appearance: in the lower jaw are holes opposite to these teeth, to receive them: when they clap their jaws together it causes a surprising noise, like that which is made by forcing a heavy plank with violence upon the ground, and may be heard at a great distance.

But what is yet more surprising to a stranger, is the incredible loud and terrifying roar, which they are capable of making, especially in the spring season, their breeding time. It most resembles very heavy distant thunder, not only shaking the air and waters, but causing the earth to tremble; and when hundreds and thousands are roaring at the same time, you can scarcely be persuaded, but that the whole globe is violently and dangerously agitated.

An old champion, who is, perhaps, absolute sovereign of a little lake or lagoon, (when fifty less than himself are obliged to content themselves with swelling and roaring in little coves round about,) darts forth from the reedy coverts all at once, on the surface of the waters, in a right line; at first seemingly as rapid as lightning, but gradually more slowly until he arrives at the centre of the lake, when he stops. He now swells himself by drawing in wind and water through his mouth, which causes a loud sonorous rattling in the throat for near a minute, but it is immediately forced out again through his mouth and nostrils, with a loud noise, brandishing his tail in the air, and the vapour ascending from his nostrils like smoke. At other times, when swollen to an extent ready to burst, his head and tail lifted up, he spins or twirls round on the surface of the water. He acts his part like an Indian chief when rehearsing his feats of war; and then retiring, the exhibition is continued by others who dare to step forth, and strive to excel each other, to gain the attention of the favourite female.

menclature and observations, and referred to your authority. To have you, therefore, to consult with in the course of this great publication, I consider a most happy and even auspicious circumstance; and I hope you will, on all occasions, be a rigid censor and kind monitor, whenever you find me deviating from the beauties of nature or the truth of description."

In fact, the rich fund of knowledge possessed by Mr. Bartram, after so many years of application and research, and the simple and unaffected manner in which he imparted instruction to those who sought it of him, made his society agreeable, and courted by the literary, scientific, and others on very many occasions, but by no one more than William Hamilton, Esq., a wealthy and highly respectable citizen of the county of Philadelphia, whose extensive domains bordering on the more humble residence of Mr. Bartram, offered him many opportunities of reaping advantages and pleasure from the instructive knowledge of the latter; Mr. Hamilton himself being fond of the study of botany. Mr. Bartram was a source of reference to many naturalists of his day, and there was scarcely an American or foreign writer who attempted the natural history of this country but applied to him for information on their relative treatises, and in many instances his generous contributions were received and diffused to the world by other writers without giving credit to the proper author.

So great was the fondness of Mr. Bartram for the works of nature, that at the advanced age of 65, he concluded to accompany Mr. Wilson on a short tour, and assist him in his work on ornithology; on this the latter placed much reliance, and his prospects of success became cheering by so valuable a companion; but a long course of inclement weather setting in, prevented the travellers from pursuing their journey on the appointed day. On this occasion Mr. Wilson composed the following stanzas, and sent them to his aged friend in form of a note:

June 16, 1804.

" I believe we had better put off our intended jaunt until some more auspicious day.

" Clouds, from eastern regions driven,
Still obscure the gloomy skies;
Let us yield, since angry heaven
Frowns upon our enterprise.

" Haply some unseen disaster
Hung impending o'er our way,
Which our kind Almighty Master
Saw, and sought us thus to stay.

" By-and-by, when fair Aurora
Bids the drowsy fogs to fly,
And the glorious god of Flora
Rises in a cloudless sky,

" Then, in whirling chariot seated,
With my friend I'll gladly go:
With his converse richly treated—
Happy to be honoured so."

Mr. Bartram was a member of the Society of Friends, but his religious opinions inclined to Unitarianism; his disposition was gentle, and his demeanour meek, but somewhat reserved. Mr. Bartram never married, and therefore had no parental duties to perform, but to those around him, he was always provident, affectionate, and kind, and benevolent to others. In stature he was below the middling size; his general health was good, although his constitution was not robust. Habituated to the study of nature, he saw nothing but mildness and harmony in all her works, and, viewing them with that philosophy which exalts and leads the mind to the contemplation of the great first cause of all, he had imparted to his feelings the serenity which was so remarkable throughout his life; this, supporting his constitution, and being exceedingly temperate in all his habits, his days were numbered beyond the boundary common to human life.

A few minutes before his death he wrote an article on the natural history of a plant, and, in rising from his desk to take a morning survey of the botanic grounds, he had proceeded only a few steps from his door when he burst a blood-vessel, which suddenly closed his useful life July 22d, 1823, in the 85th year of his age.

THE HORSE.

EQUUS CABALLUS.

Of all brute animals in a state of association with the human race, the HORSE occupies the first and most important rank. He forms an indispensable link in the chain of Creation: without him, nature's system and human enjoyments had been incomplete. He contributes equally to the services, luxuries, and pleasures of man. Whether it be laboriously to till the soil, as an associate with the patient ox, to carry the heaviest burdens, or to perform the longest and most painful journies, the Horse is the ready and obedient slave of his master. Nature has endowed this her favourite animal with a degree of intelligence and a generous inclination to obedience, which render him highly susceptible of education. His form and qualities are admirably adapted by the Eternal and Unerring Artist, to the particular rank he is intended to fill in the scale of being. He is either fashioned to sustain heavy burdens, and to endure the coarsest drudgery, or endued with that just and beautiful symmetry of form and delicacy of skin, which convey to the critical and scientific view, ideas of perfection, and which are harbingers of the highest degree of quadrupedal activity and speed. His full eye beams with mildness and generosity, or sparkles with the fire of courage, energy, and action. In war, he offers a dauntless front to the greatest dangers, engaging in the mortal strife and clangor of battle, unappalled, and as actuated by an undivided and equal interest with his rider. In the field and on the course, he exhibits a speed, and power of continuance, a firmness of nerve, a strength of muscle and elasticity of sinew, of which no other animal of the creation is capable; bearing his rider along, over plains, hills, and vallies, as if impelled by supernatural energy: but all descriptions of the Horse must give place to that inspired one of Job, which has elevated and delighted the minds of men of all ages and all nations:—

" Hast thou given the Horse strength? Hast thou clothed his neck with thunder? Canst thou make him afraid as a grasshopper? The glory of his nostrils is terrible. He paweth in the valley, and rejoiceth in his strength. He goeth on to meet the armed men. He mocketh at fear, and is not affrighted: neither turneth he his back from the sword. The quiver rattleth against him, the glittering spear and the shield. He swalloweth the ground with fierceness and rage: neither believeth he that it is the sound of the trumpet. He sayeth among the trumpets, ha! ha! and he smelleth the battle afar off, the thunder of the captains, and the shouting."

Job was a native of those desarts, to which is indigenous that fine and delicate model of the horse genus, from his superior speed, styled the COURSER. These beautiful animals are supposed to have originated in the desarts of Arabia, of Barbary, and of some other parts of Africa, and from those to have migrated to the circumjacent countries. Granting this to be supposition, it is confirmed by an unbroken evidence of facts during thousands of years, recourse being invariably had to those desarts for supplies of this matchless race: but there exists no record of sufficient antiquity to reach the first example of taming the horse, since the most ancient histories represent him as already inured to the service of man.

The noblest conquest which was ever made by man is that of this spirited and haughty animal, which shares with him the fatigues of war and the glory of the combat. Equally intrepid as his master, the Horse sees the danger, and braves it; inspired at the clash of arms, he loves it, he seeks it, and is animated with the same ardour. He feels pleasure also in the chase, in tournaments, in the course; he is all fire, but, equally tractable as courageous, does not give way to his impetuosity, and knows how to check his inclinations; he not only submits to the arm which guides him, but even seems to consult the desires of his rider; and, always obedient to the impressions which he receives from him, presses on, moves gently, or stops, and only acts as his rider pleases. The Horse is a creature which renounces his being, to exist only by the will of another, which he knows how to anticipate, and even express, and execute by the promptitude and exactness of his movements: he feels as much as we desire, does only what we wish, giving himself up without reserve, and refuses nothing, makes use of all his strength, exerts himself beyond it, and even dies the better to obey us.

Such is the Horse, whose natural qualities art has improved. His education commences with the loss of his liberty, and by constraint it is finished. The slavery or servitude of these creatures is universal, and so ancient that we rarely see them in their natural state: they are never wholly free from all their bands, not even at the time of rest; and if they are sometimes suffered to range at liberty in the fields, they always bear about them tokens of servitude, and frequently the cruel marks of servitude and of pain: the mouth is deformed by the wrinkles occasioned by the bit, the flanks scarred with wounds inflicted by the spur, the hoofs are pierced by nails, the attitude of the body constrained, from the subsisting impression of habitual shackles, from which they would be delivered in vain, as they would not be the more at liberty for it. Even those whose slavery is the most gentle, who are only fed and broken for luxury and magnificence, and whose golden chains serve less to decorate them, than to satisfy the vanity of their master, are still more dishonoured by the elegance of their trappings, by the tresses of their manes, by the gold and silk with which they are covered, than by the iron shoes on their feet.

COUGAR, OR PANTHER

THE COUGAR.

FELIS CONCOLOR.

Felis Concolor et discolor; L. Gmel. *Syst. Nat.* i. *p.* 79. *sp.* 9—12.—Temminck, *Monog de Mam. livrais* iv. *p.* 134.—*Felis Concolor,* Linnæus—Godman, *p.* 291, *vol.* i.—*Le Cougar,* Buff. *Quad. vol.* ix. *tab.* 59; *Cougar de Pennsylvanie et Cougar Noir;* Buff. *Supp.* iii. *p.* 41, 42.—*Pouma;* Garcilasso, *liv.* viii. *chap.* xviii.—*Gouzara,* De Azzara, *Quad. du Paraguay, vol.* i. *p.* 133.—*Puma;* Pennant, *Art. Zool. vol.* i. *p.* 49.—Menagerie of Living Animals, exhibited in Philadelphia, winter of 1831–2.

The interesting animal, from which our drawing is made, (and which we consider a perfect representation of the original,) is well known to the public as belonging to the celebrated menagerie of wild animals, now exhibiting in the city of Philadelphia. This Cougar was taken on Red River, near Natchitoches, in the state of Louisiana, by a hunting party, after a hard battle, in which he destroyed several dogs, and was at last secured by means of long poles, and taken to New-Orleans, where he was purchased, and added to this menagerie. He is an uncommon fine specimen of the species, and will measure eight and a half feet from the nose to the tip of the tail, and was supposed to be five years old when taken; but no treatment, either kind or severe, has subdued his disposition sufficient to permit him to be handled with safety.

There is scarcely a brute animal on earth, but will flee the face of man. Whether it is the dignity of his form, or the fear implanted in all the brute creation by the Author of their being, which causes them to acknowledge men " as the lords of creation,"—certain it is, that among even the most ferocious animals, very few can be found which will venture to attack a man; and when this is done, hunger or desperation is the exciting cause. The Cougar, when hungry, and no longer able to obtain the ordinary supplies of food, or wounded by its adversary, will attack alike both man and beast, fearless of all consequences. Its ferocity is easily excited, and when a painful wound is inflicted, its rage is terrible, and will evince the utmost determination to revenge itself.

The following anecdote, which is copied from Godman's Natural History, was furnished by the late William Scudder, who had the Cougar, and which is still in the New-York Museum.

" Two hunters, accompanied by two dogs, went out in quest of game near the Kaatskill Mountains. At the foot of a large hill, they agreed to go round it in opposite directions, and when either discharged his rifle, the other was to hasten towards him, to aid in securing the game. Soon after parting, the report of a rifle was heard by one of them, who, hastening towards the spot, after some search, found nothing but the dog, dreadfully lacerated, and dead. He now became much alarmed for the fate of his companion, and while anxiously looking around, was horror-struck by the harsh growl of a Cougar, which he perceived on a large limb of a tree, crouching on the body of his friend, and apparently meditating an attack on himself. Instantly he levelled his rifle at the beast, and was so fortunate as to wound it mortally, when it fell to the ground along with the body of his slaughtered companion. His dog then rushed upon the wounded Cougar, which, with one blow of its paw, laid the poor creature dead by its side. The surviving hunter now left the spot, and quickly returned with several other persons, when they found the lifeless Cougar extended near the dead bodies of the hunter and the faithful dogs."

In its destructive habits, the Cougar resembles the Tiger more than any other animal. The lion, and most carnivorous animals, destroy only sufficient for their present necessities, but the Tiger and Cougar are not only ferocious, but cruel, when necessity no longer requires it. After destroying their prey, they first suck the blood, and should more victims be present, go on destroying so long as subjects for destruction are within their reach. They have a thirst for blood which can hardly be satiated, and delighting so excessively in carnage, they are excited with as much energy in killing the last, as they possessed when destroying their first victim; and this prodigality of life is more strikingly manifested by the fact, that when the carcass of their prey becomes void of blood, or putrid, they forsake it entirely. It is one of those few animals whose ferocity is almost unconquerable; and when friendship and good treatment have in a measure softened its disposition, its constancy is very suspicious, and treachery is frequently manifested towards the hand which is extended in kindness towards it.

When the Cougar is aroused to madness, or in the act of springing on its prey, it usually crouches with its fore legs nearly close to the ground, and the hinder parts somewhat more elevated; the eyes are enlarged and wild, and the muscles of the face so drawn up as to bespeak great ferocity, while the light and shadows of the countenance are beautifully variegated; the ears, which usually stand upright, are now turned downward and backward, and in proportion to its anger, lie closer to the skin. Our Drawing is made from the animal while in this position, it having been excited purposely, by the appearance of the Lama belonging to the same menagerie, before its cage.

GREAT HORNED OWL

GREAT HORNED-OWL.

STRIX VIRGINIANA.

Arct. Zool. p. 228, *No.* 114.—Edw. 60.—Lath. i, 119. Turt. *Syst. p.* 166.—*Hibou des Terres Magellaniques,* Buff.—*Pl. Enl.* 385.—*Bubo Virginianus,* Briss. i, *p.* 484.—*Strix Virginiana, Ind. Orn. p.* 52.—Gmel. *Syst.* i, *p.* 287.—*Virginian Eared Owl,* Lath. *Gen. Syn. Supl.* vi, *p.* 40.—J. Doughty's *Collection.*

"This noted and formidable Owl," says Wilson, "is found in almost every quarter of the United States. His favourite residence, however, is in the dark solitudes of deep swamps, covered with a growth of gigantic timber; and here, as soon as evening draws on, and mankind retire to rest, he sends forth such sounds, as seem scarcely to belong to this world, startling the solitary pilgrim as he slumbers by his forest fire,

'Making night hideous.'

Along the mountainous shores of the Ohio, and amidst the deep forests of Indiana, alone, and reposing in the woods, this ghostly watchman frequently warned me of the approach of morning, and amused me with his singular exclamations; sometimes sweeping down and around my fire, uttering a loud and sudden *Waugh O! Waugh O!* sufficient to have alarmed a whole garrison. He has other nocturnal solos, no less melodious, one of which very strikingly resembles the half-suppressed screams of a person suffocating, or throttled, and cannot fail of being exceedingly entertaining to a lonely benighted traveller, in the midst of an Indian wilderness.

"This species inhabits the country round Hudson's Bay; and, according to Pennant, who considers it a mere variety of the Eagle Owl, (*Strix bubo*) of Europe, is found in Kamtschatka; extends even to the arctic regions, where it is often found white; and occurs as low as Astrakan. It has also been seen white in the United States; but this has doubtless been owing to disease or natural defect, and not to climate. It preys on young rabbits, squirrels, rats, mice, partridges, and small birds of various kinds. It has been often known to prowl about the farmhouse, and carry off chickens from the roost. A very large one, wing-broken while on a foraging excursion of this kind, was kept about a house for several days, and at length disappeared, no one knew how. Almost every day after this, hens and chickens also disappeared, one by one, in an unaccountable manner, till in eight or ten days very few were left remaining. The fox, the minx and weasel, were alternately the reputed authors of this mischief, until one morning, an old lady, rising before day to bake, in passing towards the oven, surprised her late prisoner the Owl, regaling himself on the body of a newly killed hen. The thief instantly made for his hole under the house, whence the enraged matron soon dislodged him with the brush-handle, and without mercy despatched him. In this snug retreat were found the greater part of the feathers, and many large fragments, of her whole family of chickens.

"There is something in the character of the Owl so recluse, solitary and mysterious, something so discordant in the tones of its voice, heard only amid the silence and gloom of night, and in the most lonely and sequestered situations, as to have strongly impressed the minds of mankind in general with sensations of awe, and abhorrence of the whole tribe. The poets have indulged freely in this general prejudice; and in their descriptions and delineations of midnight storms, and gloomy scenes of nature, the Owl is generally introduced to heighten the horror of the picture. Ignorance and superstition, in all ages, and in all countries, listen to the voice of the Owl, and even contemplate its physiognomy with feelings of disgust, and a kind of fearful awe. The priests, or conjurers, among some of our Indian nations, have taken advantage of the reverential horror for this bird, and have adopted the *Great Horned-Owl,* the subject of the present account, as the symbol or emblem of their office. 'Among the Creeks,' says Mr. Bartram, 'the junior priests, or students, constantly wear a white mantle, and have a Great Owl skin cased and stuffed very ingeniously, so well executed as almost to appear like the living bird, having large sparkling glass beads, or buttons, fixed in the head for eyes. This insignia of wisdom and divination they wear sometimes as a crest on the top of the head; at other times the image sits on the arm, or is borne on the hand. These bachelors are also distinguished from the other people by their taciturnity, grave and solemn countenance, dignified step, and singing to themselves songs or hymns in a low, sweet voice, as they stroll about the town.'

"Nothing is a more effectual cure for superstition than a knowledge of the general laws and productions of nature; nor more forcibly leads our reflections to the first, great self-existent CAUSE of all, to whom our reverential awe is then humbly devoted, and not to any of his dependent creatures. With all the gloomy habits, and ungracious tones, of the Owl, there is nothing in this bird supernatural or mysterious, or more than that of a simple bird of prey, formed for feeding by night, like many other animals, and of reposing by day. The harshness of its voice, occasioned by the width and capacity of its throat, may be intended by heaven as an alarm and warning to the birds and animals on which it preys, to secure themselves from danger. The voices of all carnivorous birds and animals are also observed to be harsh and hideous, probably for this very purpose."

CANVAS-BACK DUCK

RED-HEADED DUCK

CANVAS-BACK DUCK.

ANAS VALISINERIA.

Collection of S. P. GRIFFITTS, *Esq.*

The Canvas-back Duck arrives in the United States from the north about the middle of October; a few descend to the Hudson and Delaware, but the great body of these birds resort to the numerous rivers belonging to and in the neighbourhood of the Chesapeake Bay, particularly the Susquehanna, the Patapsco, Potomac, and James' Rivers, which appear to be their general winter rendezvous. Beyond this, to the south, I can find no certain accounts of them. At the Susquehanna they are called *Canvas-backs*, on the Potomac, *White-backs*, and on James' River, *Sheldrakes*. They are seldom found at a great distance up any of these rivers, or even in the salt water bay; but in that particular part of tide water where a certain grass-like plant grows, on the roots of which they feed. This plant, which is said to be a species of *Valisineria*, grows on fresh water shoals of from seven to nine feet, (but never where they are occasionally dry,) in long narrow grass-like blades of four or five feet in length; the root is white, and has some resemblance to small celery. This grass is in many places so thick that a boat can with difficulty be rowed through it, it so impedes the oars. The shores are lined with large quantities of it torn up by the Ducks, and drifted up by the winds, lying like hay in wind rows. Wherever this plant grows in abundance the Canvas-backs may be expected, either to pay occasional visits, or to make it their regular residence during the winter. It occurs in some parts of the Hudson; in the Delaware, near Gloucester, a few miles below Philadelphia; and in most of the rivers that fall into the Chesapeake, to each of which particular places these Ducks resort; while in waters unprovided with this nutritive plant they are altogether unknown.

On the first arrival of these birds in the Susquehanna, near Havre-de-grace, they are generally lean; but such is the abundance of their favourite food, that towards the beginning of November they are in pretty good order. They are excellent divers, and swim with great speed and agility. They sometimes assemble in such multitudes as to cover several acres of the river, and when they rise suddenly, produce a noise resembling thunder. They float about these shoals, diving and tearing up the grass by the roots, which is the only part they eat. They are extremely shy, and can rarely be approached unless by stratagem.

The Canvas-back, in the rich juicy tenderness of its flesh, and its delicacy and flavour, stands unrivalled by the whole of its tribe, in this or perhaps any other quarter of the world. Those killed in the waters of the Chesapeake are generally esteemed superior to all others, doubtless from the great abundance of their favourite food which these rivers produce. At our public dinners, hotels, and particular entertainments, the Canvas-backs are universal favourites. They not only grace but dignify the table, and their very name conveys to the imagination of the eager epicure, the most comfortable and exhilarating ideas. Hence on such occasions, it has not been uncommon to pay from one to three dollars a pair for these Ducks; and, indeed, at such times, if they can they must be had, whatever may be the price.

RED-HEADED DUCK.

ANAS FERINA.

Anas Ferina, GMEL. I. p. 530, No. 31.—*Anas rufa, Id.* p. 515.—*Ind. Orn.* p. 862, No. 77; p. 863, No. 78.— *Rufous necked-Duck, Gen. Syn.* III. p. 477, No. 32.— *Pochard, Id.* p. 523, No. 68.—*Red-headed Duck,* LAWSON's *Carolina,* p. 150.—BEWICK II. p. 320.—*Arct. Zool.* No. 491. *Br. Zool.* No. 284.—*Le Millouin,* BRISS. VI. p. 384, No. 19, pl. 35. *fig.* 1; *Le Millouin nois, Id.* p. 389, *A. young male? Le Millouin du Mexique, Id.* p. 390, No. 20, *female,* BUFF. IX. p. 216. *Pl. Enl.* 803.—TEMM. *Man. d'Orn.* p. 669.—WILLOUGHBY, p. 367, § XI.—MONTAGU, *Orn. Dict.*—PHILADELPHIA MUSEUM.

THIS is a common associate of the Canvas-back, frequenting the same places, and feeding on the *stems* of the same grass, the latter eating only the *roots;* its flesh is very little inferior, and it is often sold in our markets for the Canvas-back, to those unacquainted with the characteristic marks of each. Anxious as I am to determine precisely whether this species be the Red-headed Wigeon, Pochard, or Dun bird of England, I have not been able to ascertain the point to my own satisfaction; though I think it very probably the same, the size, extent, and general description of the Pochard agreeing pretty nearly with this.

75

BREAKING COVER

FOX-HUNTING.

BREAKING COVER.

The beauties and merits of the Chase, consist of the soul-enlivening music of the hounds, the hilarity which always prevails in the company, the intrepidity of mind, and daring boldness, which fear no obstacles, and an acquirement of so good a knowledge of horsemanship, as to surmount great difficulties, without injury to the horse or rider. The benefits are, the necessity of early rising,—the continual exercise of the body, while the mind is enlivened by passing scenes, and an emulation to excel, when the prospect of victory is pressing the expectants in joyful anticipation to the desired goal. It is neither cruel to the horse, which derives as much pleasure nearly as his rider, nor does it pursue to death a useful or innocent animal, but a thief and a destroyer.

To the fastidious mind, most field amusements are objectionable, in consequence (as it is said) of their tendency to cruelty. In Fox-hunting, however, no such objection should present itself. Most enjoyments which this life affords, are allowable to a certain extent; every thing may be overdone; and that which at one time, by moderate use, is a source of delight, may, at another time, by dissipation, be an intolerable burden; but any enjoyment which, while it increases the happiness and welfare of an individual, is also of service to a community, becomes doubly imposing, and allowable. In this sense, then, should Fox-hunting be regarded; for in the first place it can only be properly done on horseback, which gives the rider a knowledge of the horse and horsemanship, and every man who is proficient in these things, is a useful member of society, either in agriculture or war; and again, the sportsman becomes healthful and endured to hardship, while the mind, having been enlivened and made buoyant by rural enjoyments, fits the possessor more properly to fulfil the moral and social duties of life.

The interests of the Chase can only be properly appreciated by those who have mingled in its pleasures. No tongue nor pen can do justice to an interesting chase; although volumes in prose and poetry have been written by able hands and practical sportsmen, and whose descriptions have been admired by the world, but which fall far short of the reality of these soul-absorbing pleasures.

As we shall in the progress of this work, have occasion to record some very celebrated Fox-hunts. it may suffice at present, to give a few rules on Fox-hunting, selected from very high authority, from which the sportsman may glean some useful hints:—

This author remarks, that " There are certain rules that ought to be observed by a huntsman: he should always listen to his hounds whilst they are running in cover; he should be particularly attentive to the head hounds, and he should be constantly on his guard against a skirter; for, if there are two scents, he must be wrong. Generally speaking, the best scent is least likely to be that of the hunted fox, and as a fox seldom suffers hounds to run up to him, as long as he is able to prevent it, so, nine times out of ten, when foxes are hallooed early in the day, they are all fresh foxes. The hounds most likely to be right are the hard-running, line-hunting hounds; or such as the huntsman knows had the lead before there arose any doubt of changing.

" With regard to the Fox, if he breaks over an open country, it is no sign that he is hard run; for they seldom, at any time, will do that, unless they are a great way before the hounds. Also, if he runs up the wind,—foxes seldom do that when they have been long hunted and grow weak; and when they run their foil, *that* also may direct the huntsman. All this requires a good ear and nice observation; and, indeed, in these consist the chief excellence of a huntsman.

" The huntsman at a check, had better let his hounds alone, or content himself with holding them forward, without taking them off their noses. Hounds that are not used to be cast, will of themselves acquire a better cast than it is in the power of any huntsman to give them; will spread more and try better for the scent; and, if they are in health and spirits, they will want no encouragement.

" If they are at fault, and have made their own cast, which the huntsman should always encourage them to do, it is then his business to assist them further; but, except in some particular instances, they should never be cast as long as they are inclined to hunt. The first cast of a huntsman should be a regular one: if that does not succeed, he should be at liberty to follow his own opinion, and proceed as observation and genius may direct. When a knowing cast is made, there ought to be some mark of good sense or meaning in it—whether down the wind, or towards some likely cover or strong earth; however, as it is at best uncertain, and as the huntsman and the fox may be of different opinions, a regular cast should always be made before a knowing one is attempted, which, as a last resource, should not be called forth till it is wanted. The letting hounds alone is but a negative goodness in a huntsman; whereas it is true that this last gives him an opportunity of displaying genius, if he happen to possess so rare and valuable a qualification. There is one fault, however, which a knowing huntsman is apt to commit—he will find a fresh fox, and then claim the merit of having recovered the hunted one. "

ESQUIMAUX DOG.

Canis familiaris Borealis.—DESMAREST.

THIS variety of the Dog most nearly resembles the Shepherd's Dog, and the Wolf Dog. The ears are short and erect; the tail is bushy, and carried in a graceful curve over the back: in this particular, the Esquimaux Dog principally differs from the wolf of the same district, whose tail is carried between his legs in running. The tail *turned upward* is the distinguishing characteristic of the domestic Dog, of every variety. It has been considered by some naturalists, that these Dogs are wolves in a state of domestication. The anatomy of both, for the most part, corresponds; the wolf is, however, larger, and more muscular. The average height of the Esquimaux Dog is one foot, ten inches; the length of the body, from the occiput (the back of the head) to the insertion of the tail, two feet three inches; and of the tail itself, one foot, one inch. Some of the Esquimaux Dogs are brindled, some black and white, some almost entirely black, some of yellowish tinge, and some are of a dingy red. Their coat is thick and furry; the hair, in winter, being from three to four inches long: nature has also provided them with an under coating of close soft wool, at that season, which they lose in spring; so that they endure their climate with comparative comfort. They never bark; but have a long melancholy howl, like the wolf. They are familiar and domestic; but snarl and fight amongst themselves, much more than Dogs in general.

The Esquimaux, a race of people inhabiting the most northerly parts of the American continent, and the adjoining islands, are dependent upon the services of this faithful species of Dog, for most of the few comforts of their lives; for assistance in the chase; for carrying burdens; and for their rapid and certain conveyance over the trackless snows of their dreary plains. The Dogs, subjected to a constant dependance upon their masters, receiving scanty food and abundant chastisement, assist them in hunting the seal, the rein-deer, and the bear. In the summer, a single Dog carries a weight of thirty pounds, in attending his master in the pursuit of game: in winter, yoked in numbers to heavy sledges, they drag five or six persons at the rate of seven or eight miles an hour, and will perform journeys of sixty miles a day. What the rein-deer is to the Laplander, this Dog is to the Esquimaux. He is a faithful slave, who grumbles, but does not rebel; whose endurance never tires, and whose fidelity is never shaken by blows and starving. These animals are obstinate in their nature; but the women, who treat them with more kindness than the men, and who nurse them in their helpless state, or when they are sick, have an unbounded command over their affections; and can thus catch them at any time, and entice them from their huts, to yoke them to their sledges, even when they are suffering the severest hunger, and have no resource but to eat the most tough and filthy remains of animal matter which they can espy on their laborious journeys.

The Dogs of the Esquimaux offer to us a striking example of the great services which the race of Dogs has rendered to mankind in the progress of civilization. The inhabitants of the shores of Baffin's Bay, and of those still more inclement regions to which discovery ships have recently penetrated, are perhaps never destined to advance much farther than their present condition in the scale of humanity. Their climate forbids them attempting the gratification of any desires beyond the commonest animal wants. In the short summers, they hunt the rein-deer for a stock of food and clothing; during the long winter, when the stern demands of hunger drive them from their snow-huts, to search for provisions, they still find a supply in the rein-deer, in the seals, which lie in holes under the ice of the lakes, and in the bears which prowl about on the frozen shores of the sea. Without the exquisite scent and the undaunted courage of their Dogs, the several objects of their chase could never be obtained in sufficient quantities, during the winter, to supply the wants of the inhabitants; nor could the men be conveyed from place to place over the snow, with that celerity which greatly contributes to their success in hunting. In drawing the sledges, if the Dogs scent a single rein-deer, even a quarter of a mile distant, they gallop off furiously in the direction of the scent; and the animal is soon within the reach of the unerring arrow of the hunter. They will discover a seal-hole entirely by the smell, at a very great distance. Their desire to attack the ferocious bear is so great, that the word *nennook*, which signifies that animal, is often used to encourage them, when running in a sledge: two or three Dogs, led forward by a man, will fasten upon the largest bear without hesitation. They are eager to chase every animal but the wolf; and of him they appear to have an instinctive terror, which manifests itself, on his approach, in a loud and long-continued howl. Certainly there is no animal which combines so many properties useful to his master as the Dog of the Esquimaux.

ESQUIMAUX DOG

RUBY-CROWNED WREN

BLUE JAY

RUBY-CROWNED WREN.

SYLVIA CALENDULA.

[Reduced to half size.]

Le Roitelet Rubis, BUFF. v. 373.—EDW. 254.—LATH.
Syn. II. 511.—*Arct. Zool.* 320.—*Regulus cristatus
alter vertice rubini coloris*, BARTRAM, p. 292.—*Motacilla calendula*, LINN. I. p. 337.—GMEL. *Syst.* I. p.
994.—*Sylvia calendula*, LATH. *Ind. Orn.* p. 549.—
Regulus rubineus, VIEILLOT, *Ois. de l' Am. Sept.* pl.
104.—J. DOUGHTY's Collection.

THIS little bird visits us early in the spring from the
south, and is generally first found among the maple blossoms, about the beginning of April. These failing, it has
recourse to those of the peach, apple, and other fruit trees,
partly for the tops of the sweet and slender stamina of the
flowers, and partly for the winged insects that hover among
them. In the middle of summer I have rarely met with
these birds in Pennsylvania, and as they penetrate as far
north as the country round Hudson's Bay, and also breed
there, it accounts for their late arrival here in fall. They
then associate with the different species of Titmouse, and
the Golden-crested Wren; and are particularly numerous
in the month of October and beginning of November, in
orchards, among the decaying leaves of the apple trees,
that at that season are infested with great numbers of small,
black winged insects, among which they make great havoc.
I have often regretted the painful necessity one is under of
taking away the lives of such inoffensive and useful little
creatures, merely to obtain a more perfect knowledge of
the species, for they appear so busy, so active, and unsuspecting, as to continue searching about the same twig, even
after their companions have been shot down beside them.
They are more remarkably so in autumn ; which may be
owing to the great number of young and inexperienced
birds which are then among them; and frequently at this
season I have stood under the tree, motionless, to observe
them, while they gleaned among the low branches, sometimes within a foot or two of my head. They are extremely
adroit in catching their prey; have only at times a feeble
chirp; visit the tops of the tallest trees, as well as the lowest bushes; and continue generally for a considerable time
among the branches of the same tree, darting about from
place to place; appearing, when on the top of a high maple, no bigger than humble-bees.

BLUE JAY.

CORVUS CRISTATUS.

[Reduced to half size.]

LINN. *Syst.* I. p. 106, *No.* 8. *ed.* 10.—*Garrulus canadensis cœruleus*, BRISS. II. p. 55.—*Pica glandaria
cristata*, KLEIN. p. 61, 3.—*Le Geai bleu de l' Amerique
Septentrionale*, BUFF. III. p. 120. *Pl. Enl.* 529.—*Blue
Jay*, CATESB. *Car.* I. 15.—EDW. 239.—*Arct. Zool.* II.
No. 138.—LATH. *Syn.* I. p. 386, 20.—BARTRAM, p.
290.—J. DOUGHTY's Collection.

The Blue Jay is an almost universal inhabitant of the
woods, frequenting the thickest settlements, as well as the
deepest recesses of the forest, where his squalling voice often
alarms the deer, to the disappointment and mortification of
the hunter; one of whom informed me, that he made it a
point, in summer, to kill every Jay he could meet with.
In the charming season of spring, when every thicket pours
forth harmony, the part performed by the Jay always
catches the ear. He appears to be, among his fellow-mu-
sicians, what the trumpeter is in a band, some of his notes
having no distant resemblance to the tones of that instrument. These he has the faculty of changing through a
great variety of modulations, according to the particular
humour he happens to be in. When disposed to ridicule,
there is scarce a bird whose peculiarities of song he cannot
tune his notes to. When engaged in the blandishments of
love, they resemble the soft chatterings of a duck; and while
he nestles among the thick branches of the cedar, are
scarce heard at a few paces distance; but no sooner does
he discover your approach, than he sets up a sudden and
vehement outcry, flying off, and screaming with all his
might, as if he called the whole feathered tribes of the
neighbourhood to witness some outrageous usage he had
received. When he hops undisturbed among the high
branches of the oak and hickory, they become soft and
musical; and his calls of the female, a stranger would readily mistake for the repeated creakings of an ungreased
wheelbarrow. All these he accompanies with various nods,
jerks, and other gesticulations, for which the whole tribe
of Jays are so remarkable, that, with some other peculiarities, they might have very well justified the great Swedish
naturalist in forming them into a separate genus by themselves.

HUMMING BIRDS ROSE

HUMMING-BIRD.

TROCHILUS COLUBRIS.

[Male and Female—size of life.]

Trochilus colubris, Linn. *Syst.* i, *p.* 191, *No.* 12.—
L'Oiseau mouche à gorge rouge de la Caroline, Briss.
Orn. iii. *p.* 716, *No.* 13, *t.* 36, *fig* 6.—*Le Rubis,*
Buff. *Ois.* vi. *p.* 13.—*Humming-Bird,* Catesb. *Car.*
i. 65.—*Red-throated Humming-Bird,* Edw. i, 38,
male and female.—Lath. *Syn.* ii. 769, *No.* 35.—
From life.*

Nature in every department of her works seems to delight in variety; and the present subject of our history is almost as singular for its minuteness, beauty, want of song, and manner of feeding, as the Mocking-bird is for unrivalled excellence of notes, and plainness of plumage. Though this interesting and beautiful genus of birds comprehends upwards of seventy species, all of which, with very few exceptions, are natives of America and its adjacent islands, it is yet singular, that the species now before us should be the only one of its tribe that ever visits the territory of the United States.

According to the observations of my friend Mr. Abbott, of Savannah, in Georgia, who has been engaged these thirty years in collecting and drawing subjects of natural history in that part of the country, the Humming-bird makes its first appearance there, from the south, about the twenty-third of March, two weeks earlier than it does in the county of Burke, sixty miles higher up the country towards the interior; and at least five weeks sooner than it reaches this part of Pennsylvania. As it passes on to the northward as far as the interior of Canada, where it is seen in great numbers,† the wonder is excited how so feebly

constructed and delicate a little creature can make its way over such extensive regions of lakes and forests, among so many enemies, all its superiors in strength and magnitude. But its very *minuteness,* the rapidity of its flight, which almost eludes the eye, and that admirable instinct, reason, or whatever else it may be called, and daring courage which heaven has implanted in its bosom, are its guides and protectors. In these we may also perceive the reason why an all-wise Providence has made this little hero an exception to a rule which prevails almost universally through nature, viz. that the smallest species of a tribe are the most prolific. The Eagle lays one, sometimes two, eggs; the Crow five; the Titmouse seven or eight; the small European Wren fifteen; the Humming-bird *two,* and yet this latter is abundantly more numerous in America than the Wren is in Europe.

The Humming-bird is extremely fond of tubular flowers, and I have often stopped, with pleasure, to observe his manœuvres among the blossoms of the trumpet-flower. When arrived before a thicket of these that are full-blown, he poises, or suspends himself on wing, for the space of two or three seconds, so steadily, that his wings become invisible, or only like a mist; and you can plainly distinguish the pupil of his eye looking round with great quickness and circumspection; the glossy golden green of his back, and the fire of his throat, dazzling in the sun, form altogether a most interesting appearance. The position into which the body is usually thrown while in the act of thrusting the slender tubular tongue into the flower, to extract its sweets, is exhibited in the figure on the plate. When it alights, which is frequently, it always prefers the small dead twigs of a tree, or bush, where it dresses and arranges its plumage with great dexterity. The note of the male is a single chirp, not louder than that of a small cricket or grasshopper, generally uttered while passing from flower to flower, or when engaged in fight with his fellows; for when two males meet at the same bush or flower, a battle instantly takes place; and the combatants ascend in the air, chirping, darting and circling around each other, till the eye is no longer able to follow them. The conqueror, however, generally returns to the place, to reap the fruits of his victory. I have seen him attack, and for a few moments tease the King-bird; and have also seen him, in his turn, assaulted by a humble-bee, which he soon put to flight. He is one of those few birds that are universally beloved; and amidst the sweet dewy serenity of a summer's morning, his appearance among the arbours of honeysuckles, and beds of flowers, is truly interesting.

* The male Humming-bird, figured in the plate, was brought by a friend to the Editor, alive,—but in consequence of confinement became nearly exhausted, and on taking it from the cage, it was seized with paroxysms of fear so great as to become apparently lifeless; it however was restored, and remained the greater part of two days, sitting on a small twig, in the exact posture as drawn, during which time it was fed by means of a camel's hair pencil dipped in dissolved rock candy, until sufficient strength was gained, when it took its final leave by flying out of the window.—[Ed.]

† Mr. M'Kenzie speaks of seeing a "beautiful Humming-bird" near the head of the Unjigah or Peace River, in lat. 54°; but has not particularized the species.

RACCOON

THE RACCOON.

PROCYON LOTOR.

Ursus Lotor; Lin. Erxl. Bodd.—*Vulpes Americana;*
Charleton.—*Le Raton;* Buff. Hist. Nat. 8, pl. 43.
—*Procyon Lotor;* Cuv. Reg. An. p. 143. Sabine app.
p. 649.—*Coati Brasiliensium;* Klein.—*Mapach, etc.*
Mexicanorum.—Menagerie of Living Animals, ex-
hibited in Philadelphia, winter of 1831–2.

Were we to form an opinion of this animal's character
solely from external appearances, the mingled expression of
sagacity and innocence exhibited in his aspect, his personal
neatness and gentle movements, might all incline us to
believe that he possessed a guileless and placable disposition. But in this, as in most other cases where judg-
ments are formed without sufficient examination, we should
be in error, and find, that to the capricious mischievous-
ness of the monkey, the Raccoon adds a blood-thirsty and
vindictive spirit peculiarly his own. In the wild state,
this sanguinary appetite frequently leads to his own destruction, which his nocturnal habits might otherwise
avert; but as he slaughters the tenants of the poultry-yard
with indiscriminate ferocity, the vengeance of the plun-
dered farmer speedily retaliates on him the death so liberally dealt among the feathered victims. This destructive
propensity of the Raccoon is more remarkable, when we
observe that his teeth are not unsuited for eating fruits.
When he destroys wild or domesticated birds, he puts to
death a great number, without consuming any part of them,
except the head, or the blood which is sucked from the
neck.

The Raccoon is an excellent climber, and his strong
sharp claws effectually secure him from being shaken off
the branches of trees. In fact, so tenaciously does this
animal hold to any surface upon which it can make an
impression with its claws, that it requires a considerable
exertion of a man's strength to drag him off; and as long
as even a single foot remains attached, he continues to
cling with great force. I have had frequent occasion to
pull a Raccoon from the top of a board-fence, where there
was no projection which he could seize by; yet, such was
the power and obstinacy with which the points of his claws
were stuck into the board, as repeatedly to oblige me to
desist for fear of tearing his skin, or otherwise doing him
injury by the violence necessary to detach his hold.

The circumstance which has procured for the Raccoon
the specific name of *"Lotor,"* or the *Washer,* is very
remarkable and interesting: this is, the habit of plunging
its food into water, as if for the purpose of soaking
or cleansing it. To account for this disposition, some
naturalists have supposed that the Raccoon is not as liberally supplied with salivary organs as other animals, and
is therefore obliged to prepare its food by softening it in
water. The Raccoon, however, does not invariably wait
to subject his food to this preparation, but frequently
devours it in the condition he receives it, although it may
be nothing but dry bread, and clean water be within a
few steps of where he stands.

Water seems to be essential to their comfort, if not of
absolute necessity for the preparation of their food. I
have had for some time, and at the moment of writing
this have yet, a male and female Raccoon in the yard.
Their greatest delight appears to be dabbling in water, of
which a large tub is always kept nearly full for their use.
They are frequently seen sitting on the edge of this tub,
very busily engaged in playing with a piece of broken
china, glass, or a small cake of ice. When they have any
substance which sinks, they both paddle with their fore-
feet with great eagerness, until it is caught, and then it is
held by one, with both paws, and rubbed between them;
or a struggle ensues for the possession of it, and when it
is dropped the same sport is renewed. The coldest weather in winter does not in the least deter them from thus
dabbling in the water for amusement; nor has this action
much reference to their feeding, as it is performed at any
time, even directly after feeding, till satiated. I have
frequently broken the ice on the surface of their tub, late
at night, in the very coldest winter weather, and they have
both left their sleeping place with much alacrity, to stand
paddling the fragments of ice about, with their fore-legs in
the water nearly up to the breast. Indeed, these animals
have never evinced the slightest dislike to cold, or suffered
in any degree therefrom: they have in all weathers slept
in a flour-barrel thrown on its side, with one end entirely
open, and without any material of which to make a bed.
They show no repugnance to being sprinkled or dashed
with water, and voluntarily remain exposed to the rain or
snow, which wets them thoroughly, notwithstanding their
long hair, which being almost erect, is not well suited to
turn the rain. These Raccoons are very fond of each
other, and express the greatest delight on meeting after
having been separated for a short time, by various movements, and by hugging and rolling one another about on
the ground.

MARYLAND YELLOW-THROAT   AMERICAN REDSTART

MARYLAND YELLOW-THROAT.

SYLVIA MARILANDICA.

[Size of life.]

Turdus Trichas, LINN. *Syst.* I. 293.—EDW. 237.—
Yellow-breasted Warbler, Arct. Zool. II. No. 283. *Id.*
284.—*Le Figuier aux joues noires*, BUFF. v. 292.—
La Fauvette a poitrine jaune de la Louisiane, BUFF.
v. 162. *Pl. Enl.* 709, *fig.* 2.—LATH. *Syn.* IV.—J.
DOUGHTY's Collection.

THIS is one of the humble inhabitants of briars, brambles, alder bushes, and such shrubbery as grow most luxuriantly in low watery situations, and might with propriety be denominated *Humility*, its business or ambition seldom leading it higher than the tops of the underwood. Insects and their larvæ are its usual food. It dives into the deepest of the thicket, rambles among the roots, searches round the stems, examines both sides of the leaf, raising itself on its legs so as to peep into every crevice; amusing itself at times with a very simple, and not disagreeable, song or twitter, *whititee, whititee, whititee;* pausing for half a minute or so, and then repeating its notes as before. It inhabits the whole United States from Maine to Florida, and also Louisiana; and is particularly numerous in the low swampy thickets of Maryland, Pennsylvania, and New-Jersey. It is by no means shy; but seems deliberate and unsuspicious, as if the places it frequented, or its own diminutiveness, were its sufficient security.

AMERICAN REDSTART.

MUSCICAPA RUTICILLA.

[Size of life.]

Muscicapa Ruticilla, LINN. *Syst.* I. 236, 10.—GMEL.
Syst. I. 935.—*Motacilla flavicauda*, GMEL. *Syst.* I.
997. *(female.)—Le Gobemouche d'Amerique*, BRISS.
Orn. II. 383, 14. *Pl. Enl.* 566, *fig.* 1, 2.—*Small American Redstart*, EDW. 80, *Id.* 257. *(female.)—Yellow-tailed Warbler, Arct. Zool.* II. No. 301. *Id.* II. No.
282.—LATHAM *Syn.* IV. 427, 18.—*Arct. Zool.* II. No.
301.—J. DOUGHTY's Collection.

THOUGH this bird has been classed by several of our most respectable ornithologists, among the Warblers, yet in no species are the characteristics of the genus *Muscicapa* more decisively marked; and in fact it is one of the most expert Flycatchers of its tribe. It is almost perpetually in motion; and will pursue a retreating party of flies from the tops of the tallest trees, in an almost perpendicular but zig-zag direction, to the ground, while the clicking of its bill is distinctly heard, and I doubt not but it often secures ten or twelve of these in a descent of three or four seconds. It then alights on an adjoining branch, traverses it lengthwise for a few moments, flirting its expanded tail from side to side, and suddenly shoots off, in a direction quite unexpected, after fresh game, which it can discover at a great distance. Its notes, or twitter, though animated and sprightly, are not deserving the name of song; sometimes they are *weese, weese, weese,* repeated every quarter of a minute, as it skips among the branches; at other times this twitter varies to several other chants, which I can instantly distinguish in the woods, but cannot find words to imitate.

The name Redstart, evidently derived from the German *Rothsterts*, (red tail,) has been given this bird from its supposed resemblance to the Redstart of Europe, (*Motacilla phoenicurus;*) but besides being decisively of a different genus, it is very different both in size and in the tints and disposition of the colours of its plumage. Buffon goes even so far as to question whether the differences between the two be more than what might be naturally expected from change of climate. This eternal reference of every animal of the New World to that of the old, if adopted to the extent of this writer, with all the transmutations it is supposed to have produced, would leave us in doubt whether even the *Ka-te-dids* of America, (a species of Gryllus, well known for its lively chatter during the evenings and nights of September and October,) were not originally Nightingales of the old world, degenerated by the inferiority of the food and climate of this upstart continent. We have in America many different species of birds that approach so near in resemblance to one another, as not to be distinguished but by the eye of a naturalist, and on a close comparison; these live in the same climate, feed on the same food, and are, I doubt not, the same now as they were five thousand years ago; and ten thousand years hence, if the species then exist, will be found marked with the same nice discriminations as at present. Is it therefore surprising, that two different species, placed in different quarters of the world, should have certain near resemblances to one another, without being bastards, or degenerated descendants, the one of the other, when the whole chain of created beings seem united to each other by such amazing gradations, that bespeak, not random chance and accidental degeneracy, but the magnificent design of an incomprehensively wise and omnipotent Creator?

BIRDS' EGGS,

AND DESCRIPTION OF NESTS.

1. *Black Skimmer.*

THE nest is a mere hollow, formed in the sand, without any materials. The female lays three eggs, almost exactly oval, of a dirty white, marked with large spots of brownish black, and intermixed with others of pale Indian ink. These eggs measure one inch and three quarters, by one inch and a quarter. Half a bushel and more of eggs has sometimes been collected from one sand-bar, within the compass of half an acre. These eggs have something of a fishy taste; but are eaten by many people on the coast. The female sits on them only during the night, or in wet and stormy weather. The young remain for several weeks before they are able to fly; are fed with great assiduity by both parents; and seem to delight in lying with loosened wings, flat on the sand, enjoying its invigorating warmth. They breed but once in the season.

2. *Lesser Tern.*

About the twenty-fifth of May, or beginning of June, the female begins to lay. The eggs are dropt on the dry and warm sand, the heat of which, during the day, is fully sufficient for the purpose of incubation. This heat is sometimes so great, that one can scarcely bear the hand in it for a few moments, without inconvenience. The wonder would therefore be the greater, should the bird sit on her eggs during the day, when her warmth is altogether unnecessary, and perhaps injurious, than that she should cover them only during the damps of night, and in wet and stormy weather. They are generally four in number, and placed on the flat sands, safe beyond the reach of the highest summer tide. They are of a yellowish brown colour, blotched with rufous, and measure nearly an inch and three-quarters in length.

3. *Piping Plover.*

The nests of these birds are formed with little art; being merely shallow concavities dug in the sand, in which the eggs are laid, and, during the day at least, left to the influence of the sun to hatch them. The parents, however, always remain near the spot to protect them from injury, and probably, in cold rainy or stormy weather, to shelter them with their bodies. The eggs are three, sometimes four, large for the bird, of a dun clay colour, and marked with numerous small spots of reddish purple. A flat, dry sandy beach, just beyond the reach of the summer tides, is their favourite place for breeding.

4. *Meadow Lark.*

The nest of this species is built generally in, or below, a thick tuft or tussock of grass; it is composed of dry grass, and fine bent laid at bottom, and wound all around, leaving an arched entrance level with the ground; the inside is lined with fine stalks of the same materials, disposed with great regularity. The eggs are four, sometimes five, bluish white, marked with specks and several large blotches of reddish brown, chiefly at the thick end.

5. *Brown Thrush.*

Early in May, this bird builds its nest, choosing a thorn bush, low cedar, thicket of briars, dogwood sapling, or cluster of vines for its situation, generally within a few feet of the ground, and not unfrequently on the ground, at the foot of a small bush. Outwardly it is constructed of small sticks; then layers of dry leaves; and lastly lined with fine fibrous roots, but without any plaster. The eggs are five, thickly sprinkled with ferruginous grains. They generally have two brood in a season.

6. *Red-bird, or Cardinal Grosbeak.*

Early in May they begin to prepare their nest, which is very often fixed in a hollow, cedar, or laurel bush. Outwardly it is constructed of small twigs, tops of dry weeds, and slips of vine bark, and lined with stalks of fine grass. The female lays four eggs, thickly marked all over with touches of brownish olive, on a dull white ground; and they usually raise two brood in the season.

7. *Robin.*

The Robin builds a large nest, often on apple and cedar trees, plasters it in the inside with mud, and lines it with hay or fine grass. The female lays five eggs of a beautiful sea green.

8. *Chipping Sparrow.*

The Chipping-bird builds its nest most commonly in cedar bushes, and apple-trees, and lines it thickly with cow-hair. The female lays four or five eggs of a light blue colour, with a few dots of purplish black near the great end.

9. *Purple Grakle.*

On the tallest cedar and pine trees they generally build their nests in company, about the beginning or middle of April; sometimes ten or fifteen nests being on the same tree, and measure five inches in diameter within, and four in depth; are composed outwardly of mud, mixed with long stalks and roots of a knotty kind of grass, and lined with fine bent and horse hair. The eggs are five, of a bluish olive colour, marked with large spots and straggling streaks of black and dark brown, also with others of a fainter tinge. They rarely produce more than one brood in a season. The trees where these birds build are often at no great distance from the farm-house, and overlook the plantations.

10. *King Bird.*

The King bird builds his nest very often on the horizontal branch of an apple tree; frequently also, as Catesby observes, on a sassafras tree, at no great height from the ground, and on pear trees. The outside consists of small slender twigs, tops of withered flowers of the plant yarrow, and others, well wove together with tow and wool; and is made large, and remarkably firm and compact. It is usually lined with fine dry fibrous grass, and horse hair. The eggs are five, of a very pale cream colour, or dull white, marked with a few large spots of deep purple, and other smaller ones of light brown, chiefly, though not altogether, towards the great end. They generally build twice in the season.

11. *Cat Bird.*

This bird builds its nest about the beginning of May. The place chosen for this purpose is generally a thicket of briars or brambles, a thorn bush, thick vine, cedar, or the fork of a small sapling; no great solicitude is shown for concealment, though few birds appear more interested for the safety of their nest and young. The materials are dry leaves and weeds, small twigs and fine dry grass; the inside is lined with the fine black fibrous roots of some plant. The female lays four, sometimes five eggs, of a uniform greenish blue colour, without any spots. They generally raise two, and sometimes three brood in a season.

12. *Blue Bird.*

About the middle of March, the Blue bird is seen, accompanied by his mate, visiting the box in the garden, or the hole in the old apple-tree, the cradle of some generations of his ancestors; and as soon as the spot is fixed on, they begin to clean out the old nest, and the rubbish of the former year, and to prepare for the reception of their future offspring.

The female lays five, and sometimes six eggs, of a pale blue colour; and raises two, and sometimes three broods in a season; the male taking the youngest under his particular care while the female is again sitting.

13. *Song Sparrow.*

The Song Sparrow builds in the ground, under a tuft of grass; the nest is formed of fine dry grass, and lined with horse hair; the eggs are four or five, thickly marked with spots of reddish brown on a bluish white ground; if not interrupted, it raises three broods in the season. Nests with young have been found as early as the twenty-sixth of April, and as late as the twelfth of August. What is singular, the same bird often fixes its nest in a cedar tree, five or six feet from the ground.

14. *Swamp Blackbird.*

About the twentieth of March, or earlier if the season be open, they appear in the middle states, in numerous though small parties, and frequent the low borders of creeks, swamps, and ponds, till about the middle of April, when they separate in pairs to breed; and about the last week in April, or first in May, begin to construct their nest. The place chosen for this is generally within the precincts of a marsh or swamp, meadow, or other like watery situation. The spot usually a thicket of alder bushes, at the height of six or seven feet from the ground; sometimes in a detached bush in a meadow of high grass; often in a tussock of rushes of coarse rank grass; and not unfrequently in the ground. In all of which situations they are found. When in a bush they are generally composed outwardly of wet rushes picked from the swamp, and long tough grass in large quantity, and well lined with very fine bent. The rushes, forming the exterior, are generally extended to several of the adjoining twigs, round which they are repeatedly and securely twisted: a precaution absolutely necessary for its preservation on account of the flexible nature of the bushes in which it is placed. The same caution is observed when a tussock is chosen, by fastening the tops together, and intertwining the materials of which the nest is formed with the stalks of rushes around. When placed in the ground, less care and fewer materials being necessary, the nest is much simpler and slighter than before. The female lays five eggs, of a very pale light blue, marked with faint tinges of light purple and long straggling lines and dashes of black. It is not uncommon to find several nests in the same thicket, within a few feet of each other.

15. *Cow Bunting.*

The most remarkable trait in the character of this species is the unaccountable practice it has of dropping its eggs into the nests of other birds, instead of building and hatching for itself; and thus entirely abandoning its progeny to the care and mercy of strangers.

About the twenty-fifth of March, or early in April, the Cow-pen Bird makes his first appearance from the south, sometimes in company with the Red-winged Blackbird, more frequently in detached parties, resting early in the morning, an hour at a time, on the tops of trees near streams of water, appearing solitary, silent and fatigued. They continue to be occasionally seen, in small solitary parties, particularly along creeks and banks of rivers, so late as the middle of June; after which we see no more of them until about the beginning or middle of October, when they re-appear in much larger flocks.

Those that pass in May and June, are frequently observed loitering singly about solitary thickets, reconnoitering, no doubt, for proper nurses, to whose care they may commit the hatching of their eggs, and the rearing of their helpless orphans. Among the birds selected for this duty are the following:—the Blue-bird, the Chipping Sparrow, the Golden-crowned Thrush, the Red-eyed Flycatcher, the Yellow-bird, the Maryland Yellow-throat, the White-eyed Flycatcher, the small Blue Gray Flycatcher, and the Black and White Creeper; and, no doubt, many others, to whom the same charge is committed.

There is never but one egg of the Cow Bunting dropped in the same nest. This egg is somewhat larger than that of the Blue bird, thickly sprinkled with grains of pale brown and gray on a dirty white ground. It is of a size proportionable to that of the bird.

16. *Barn Swallow.*

Early in May the Barn Swallow builds its nest. From the size and structure of the nest, it is nearly a week before it is completely finished. It is in the form of an inverted cone, with a perpendicular section cut off on that side by which it adhered to the wood. At the top it has an extension of the edge, or offset, for the male or female to sit on occasionally, as appears by the dung; the upper diameter is about six inches by five, the height externally seven inches. This shell is formed of mud, mixed with fine hay as plasterers do their mortar with hair, to make it adhere the better; the mud seems to be placed in regular strata, or layers, from side to side; the hollow of this cone, (the shell of which is about an inch in thickness,) is filled with fine hay, well stuffed in; above that is laid a handful of very large downy geese feathers; the eggs are five, white, specked and spotted all over with reddish brown. Owing to the semi-transparency of the shell, the eggs have a slight tinge of flesh colour. The whole weighs about two pounds. The situation of these nests is generally on the pin which unites the rafters together.

They have generally two broods in the season. The first make their appearance about the second week in June; and the last brood leave the nest about the tenth of August.

19. *White-Eyed Flycatcher.*

This bird builds a very neat little nest, often in the figure of an inverted cone; it is suspended by the upper edge of the two sides, on the circular bend of a prickly vine, a species of Smilax that generally grows in low thickets. Outwardly it is constructed of various light materials, bits of rotten wood, fibres of dry stalks, of weeds, pieces of paper, commonly newspapers, an article almost always found about its nest; all these substances are interwoven with the silk of caterpillars, and the inside is lined with fine dry grass and hair. The female lays five eggs, pure white, marked near the great end with a very few small dots of deep brown or purple. They generally raise two brood in a season. They seem particularly attached to thickets of this species of Smilax, and make a great ado when any one comes near their nest; approaching within a few feet, looking down, and scolding with great vehemence.

18. *House Wren.*

This well known and familiar bird arrives about the middle of April; and about the eighth or tenth of May begins to build its nest, sometimes in the wooden cornice under the eaves, or in a hollow cherry tree, but most commonly in small boxes, fixed on the top of a pole, in or near the garden, to which he is extremely partial, for the

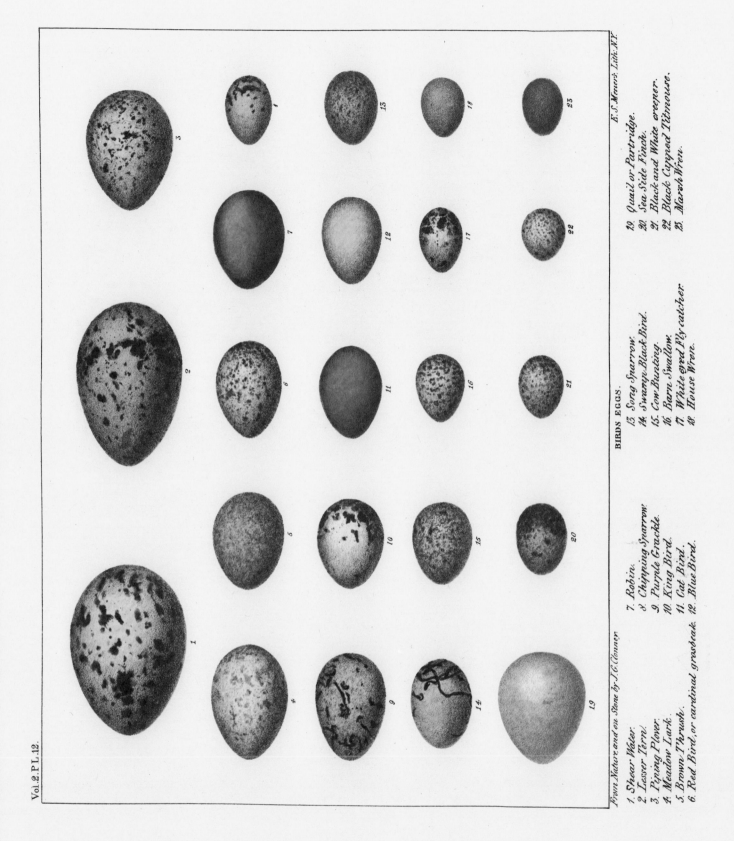

From Nature and on Stone by J.C. Conner.

E.S. Meuers Lith: N.Y.

BIRDS EGGS.

1. Shear Water.
2. Lesser Tern.
3. Piping Plover.
4. Meadow Lark.
5. Brown Thrush.
6. Red Bird, or cardinal grosbeak.

7. Robin.
8. Chipping Sparrow.
9. Purple Grackle.
10. King Bird.
11. Cat Bird.
12. Blue Bird.

13. Song Sparrow.
14. Swamp Black Bird.
15. Cow Bunting.
16. Barn Swallow.
17. White eyed Fly catcher.
18. House Wren.

19. Quail or Partridge.
20. Sea Side Finch.
21. Black and White creeper.
22. Black Capped Titmouse.
23. Marsh Wren.

Chinchilla.

great number of caterpillars and other larvæ with which it constantly supplies him. If all these conveniences are wanting, he will even put up with an old hat, nailed on the weather-boards, with a small hole for entrance; and if even this be denied him, he will find some hole, corner, or crevice, about the house, barn, or stable, rather than abandon the dwellings of man. The twigs with which the outward parts of the nest are constructed are short and crooked that they may the better hook in with one another, and the hole or entrance is so much shut up to prevent the intrusion of snakes or cats, that it appears almost impossible the body of the bird could be admitted; within this is a layer of fine dried stalks of grass, and lastly feathers. The eggs are six or seven, and sometimes nine, of a red purplish flesh colour, innumerable fine grains of that tint being thickly sprinkled over the whole egg. They generally raise two brood in a season; the first about the beginning of June, the second in July.

19. *Quail, or Partridge.*

The Quail begins to build early in May. The nest is made on the ground, usually at the bottom of a thick tuft of grass that shelters and conceals it. The materials and leaves are fine dry grass, in considerable quantity. It is well covered above, and an opening left on one side for entrance. The female lays from fifteen to twenty-four eggs, of a pure white without any spots.

20. *Sea-Side Finch.*

The nest of this species is found along the margins of the sea and salt water inlets, and is built among the tall grass and rushes common to these parts; the materials are externally of coarse salt grass, and inside of the smaller fibres of the same article; the eggs are four or five in number, and of a light blue ground, thickly sprinkled with dark brown spots, more particularly at the great end.

21. *Black and White Creeper.*

This bird completes its nest about the middle of May, and is generally fixed on the ground, at the root of a bush or sapling, and is composed externally of leaves, and inside of slight layers of cow or horse hair; no other substances compose its nest. The eggs are five in number, of a pale flesh colour, sprinkled thickly with light reddish brown spots. This nest is also a receptacle for the eggs of the Cow Bunting.

22. *Black-Capt Titmouse.*

About the middle of April, these birds begin to build, choosing the deserted hole of a squirrel or woodpecker, and sometimes with incredible labour digging out one for themselves. The female lays six white eggs, marked with minute specks of red; the first brood appears about the beginning of June, and the second towards the end of July.

23. *Marsh Wren.*

This little bird excels in the art of *design*, and constructs a nest, which, in durability, warmth, and convenience, is scarcely inferior to one, and far superior to many other birds. This is formed outwardly of wet rushes mixed with mud, well intertwisted, and fashioned into the form of a cocoa nut. A small hole is left two-thirds up, for entrance, the upper edge of which projects like a pent house over the lower, to prevent the admission of rain. The inside is lined with fine soft grass, and sometimes feathers; and the outside, when hardened by the sun, resists every kind of weather. This nest is generally suspended among the reeds, above the reach of the highest tides, and is tied so fast in every part to the surrounding reeds, as to bid defiance to the winds and the waves. The eggs are usually six, of a dark fawn colour, and very small. The young leave the nest about the twentieth of June, and they generally have a second brood in the same season.

93

SCARLET TANAGER   BLUE EYED YELLOW WARBLER

SCARLET TANAGER.

TANAGRA RUBRA.

[Size of life.]

Tanagra rubra, Linn. *Syst.* i. *p* 314, 3.—*Cardinal de Canada*, Briss. *Orn.* iii. *p.* 48, *Pl.* 2, *fig.* 5.—Lath. ii. *p.* 217, *No.* 3.—*Scarlet Sparrow*, Edw. *Pl.* 343.— *Canada Tanager, and Olive Tanager, Arct. Zool. p.* 369, *No.* 237–238.—J. Doughty's Collection.

This is one of the gaudy foreigners, (and perhaps the most showy,) that regularly visit us from the torrid regions of the south. He is drest in the richest scarlet, set off with the most jetty black, and comes, over extensive countries, to sojourn for a time among us.

On or about the first of May this bird makes his appearance in Pennsylvania. He spreads over the United States, and is found even in Canada. He rarely approaches the habitations of man, unless perhaps to the orchard, where he sometimes builds; or to the cherry trees in search of fruit. The depth of the woods is his favourite abode. There, among the thick foliage of the tallest trees, his simple and almost monotonous notes *chip, churr,* repeated at short intervals, in a pensive tone, may be occasionally heard; which appear to proceed from a considerable distance though the bird be immediately above you; a faculty bestowed on him by the beneficent Author of Nature, no doubt for his protection, to compensate in a degree for the danger to which his glowing colour would often expose him.

Among all the birds that inhabit our woods, there is none that strike the eye of a stranger, or even a native, with so much brilliancy as this. Seen among the green leaves, with the light falling strongly on his plumage, he really appears beautiful. If he has little of melody in his notes to charm us, he has nothing in them to disgust. His manners are modest, easy, and inoffensive. He commits no depredations on the property of the husbandman; but rather benefits him by the daily destruction in spring of many noxious insects; and when winter approaches he is no plundering dependant, but seeks in a distant country for that sustenance which the severity of the season denies to his industry in this. He is a striking ornament to our rural scenery, and none of the meanest of our rural songsters. Such being the true traits of his character, we shall always with pleasure welcome this beautiful, inoffensive stranger, to our orchards, groves, and forests.

BLUE-EYED YELLOW WARBLER.

SYLVIA CITRINELLA.

[Size of life.]

Yellow-poll Warbler, Lath. *Syn. v.* ii. *p.* 515, *No.* 148.— *Arct. Zool. p.* 402, *No.* 292.—*Le Figuier tachete*, Buff. *Ois.* v. *p.* 285.—*Motacilla æstiva*, Turton's *Syst. p.* 615.—*Parus luteus, Summer Yellow-bird*, Bartram, *p.* 292.—*Motacilla æstiva*, Gmel. *Syst.* i. *p.* 996.—*Sylvia æstiva*, Lath. *Ind. Orn.* ii. *p.* 551.— Vieill. *Ois. de l'Am. Sept. pl.* 95.—*Motacilla albicollis*, Gmel. *Syst.* i. *p.* 983, young.—*Sylvia albicollis*, Lath. *Ind. Orn.* ii. *p.* 535, young.—*Ficedula Canadensis*, Briss. iii. *p.* 492, 51, *t.* 26, *fig.* 3, male adult.— *Ficedula dominicensis*, Briss. iii. *p.* 494, 52, *t.* 26, f. 5.—*Figuier de Canada*, Buff. *Pl. Enl.* 58, f. 2, adult male.—J. Doughty's Collection.

This is a very common summer species, and appears almost always actively employed among the leaves and blossoms of the willows, snow-ball shrub, and poplars, searching after small green caterpillars, which are its principal food. It has a few shrill notes, uttered with emphasis, but not deserving the name of song. It arrives in Pennsylvania about the beginning of May, and departs again for the south about the middle of September. According to Latham, it is numerous in Guiana, and is also found in Canada. It is a very sprightly, unsuspicious, and familiar little bird; is often seen in and about gardens, among the blossoms of fruit trees and shrubberies; and, on account of its colour, is very noticeable. Its nest is built with great neatness, generally in the triangular fork of a small shrub, near, or among briar bushes. Outwardly it is composed of flax or tow, in thick circular layers, strongly twisted round the twigs that rise through its sides, and lined within with hair, and the soft downy substances from the stalks of fern. The eggs are four or five, of a dull white, thickly sprinkled near the great end, with specks of pale brown. They raise two broods in the season. This little bird, like many others, will feign lameness to draw you away from its nest, stretching out his neck, spreading and bending down his tail until it trails along the branch, and fluttering feebly along to draw you after him; sometimes looking back to see if you are following him, and returning back to repeat the same manœuvres, in order to attract your attention. The male is most remarkable for this practice.

GREY FOX

GRAY FOX.

CANIS CINEREO-ARGENTATUS.

Renard Gris: BRISS. *quad. p.* 41.—*Agourachay:* AZARA, *quad due Paraguay,* I. *p.* 317. *Canis Cenereo argentatus.* GMEL. SABINE, *Zool. app. p.* 657. GODMAN, vol. I. *p.* 280.—*Fulvous-necked Fox.* SHAW, *Zool. Miscel.*

THE Gray Fox is an inhabitant of all parts of the United States, from Louisiana to Canada, and as far west as the Rocky Mountains—its chief abode, however, is about human habitations, where it is more destructive than the other species. They are more numerous in the Southern States, more particularly Virginia, and form the chief source of amusement to the sportsmen of that state.

The Gray differs from the Red Fox in many particulars, although some writers make it only a variety of the latter, and indeed confound the whole race together, attributing the difference only to changes of climate and circumstances. The Gray Fox is different in colour and in many of its habits, and possesses more cunning and less disposition to wander than the Red Fox. The latter is more active and savage in its disposition, and although exceedingly carnivorous, is not so destructive to domestic animals as the Gray Fox, and emits an odour extremely offensive, which does not belong to the latter.

The Fox appears to be spread over the whole earth, and is known by most of the inhabitants of every country, and in every country differs in colour, varying as Gray, Brown, Red, Blue, Black, Silver, and in the severe climes of the arctic regions, purely white. He is one of those animals of which we have the earliest notice in sacred writ; his cunning is proverbial, and his wiles have earned for him a reputation, which would imply more than mere instinct. A writer remarks, that "in Japan, where the Fox is very common, the natives believe him to be animated with the devil; and their histories and sacred writings are filled with strange accounts respecting him." It is not, however, necessary to have recourse to heathenish traditions respecting the artfulness of this common enemy; we have him at our very doors, and his frequent depredations are convincing enough, that he possesses more than ordinary share of sagacity and mischief. He indeed appears to dwell in enmity with all animals, and unhesitatingly makes war against them, who, in return, hold him as an outlaw, and show no mercy where mercy is not to be found. Man pursues him with untiring perseverance unto death; the dog, his most formidable foe, hunts him with savage acrimony, and yelling without intermission, the death-notes of revenge. The wolf is as destructive, but a more necessitous enemy than the dog. The eagle, the crow, the jay, and many smaller birds, attend him as their mortal enemy, with signals of hatred and revenge. He appears to be an isolated being, and did he not possess that energy and cunning which nature has so bountifully given him, his race would have long since been annihilated.

The Fox is not only very voracious, but also most unmerciful in his destructive habits, and there is scarcely a living creature that he encounters, and is able to master, but he will destroy. No domestic fowl can escape his pursuit; young rabbits are his chief delight; he will draw the old ones from their seats, and pheasants and partridges from their nests, and devour them; geese, ducks, and all species of winged game, fall beneath his voracity; and when such food fails him, he will destroy rats, mice, snakes, frogs, lizards, and insects: he is an expert fisher, and where these abound, he never fails to get a plentiful supply of food.

Of all animals, none seem so well adapted for the sporting world as the Fox, and, as the subject of our present notice possesses a larger share of cunning than the other species, he seems to be pursued by hunters in preference. The very craftiness of his nature fits him well for the ingenious and persecuting spirit of man.

The Fox prepares a den or burrow under ground, mostly beside a bank, or hill, to which he retreats in case of danger or necessity, but is very fond of reposing above ground, and basking in the sun. It is said they continue to grow for eighteen months, and will live in freedom fourteen or fifteen years, but pine away and die in a much shorter period if in a state of confinement.

BLUE CRANE, OR HERON.

Arct. Zool. No. 351.—Catesby, i, 76.—*Le Crabier bleu* Buff. vii. 398.—Sloan. *Jam.* ii, 315.—Lath. *Syn. v. 3 p.* 78, No 45,—*p.* 79, *var. A.*—*Ardea cœrulescens,* Turt. *Syst. p.* 379.—*Heron bluatre de Cayenne,* Buff. *Pl. Enl.* 349, *adult.*—Philadelphia *Museum.*

In mentioning this species in his translation of the *Systema Naturæ,* Turton has introduced what he calls two *varieties,* one from New Zealand, the other from Brazil; both of which, if we may judge by their size and colour, appear to be entirely different and distinct species; the first being green, with yellow legs, the last nearly one half less than the present. By this loose mode of discrimination, the precision of science being altogether dispensed with, the whole tribe of Cranes, Herons, and Bitterns, may be styled mere *varieties* of the genus *Ardea.* The same writer has still farther increased this confusion, by designating as a different species his *Bluish Heron (A. cœrulescens,)* which agrees almost exactly with the present. Some of these mistakes may probably have originated from the figure of this bird given by Catesby, which appears to have been drawn and coloured, not from nature, but from the glimmering recollections of memory, and is extremely erroneous. These remarks are due to truth, and necessary to the elucidation of the history of his species, which seems to be but imperfectly known in Europe.

The Blue Heron is properly a native of the warmer climates of the United States, migrating thence, at the approach of winter, to the tropical regions; being found in Cayenne, Jamaica, and Mexico. On the muddy shores of the Mississippi, from Baton Rouge downwards to New Orleans, these birds are frequently met with. In spring they extend their migrations as far north as New England, chiefly in the vicinity of the sea; becoming more rare as they advance to the north. On the sea-beach of Cape May, I found a few of them breeding among the cedars, in company with the Snowy Heron, Night Heron, and Green Bittern. Their nests were composed of small sticks, built in the tops of the red cedars, and contained five eggs of a light blue colour, and of somewhat a deeper tint than those of the Night Heron. Little or no difference could be perceived between the colours and markings of the male and female. This remark is applicable to almost the whole genus; though from the circumstance of many of the yearling birds differing in plumage, they have been mistaken for females.

The Blue Heron, though in the northern states it is found chiefly in the neighbourhood of the ocean, probably on account of the greater temperature of the climate, is yet particularly fond of fresh water bogs, on the edges of the salt marsh. These it often frequents, wading about in search of tadpoles, lizards, various larvæ of winged insects and mud worms. It moves actively about in search of these, sometimes making a run at its prey; and is often seen in company with the Snowy Heron. Like this last, it is also very silent, intent and watchful.

The genus Ardea is the most numerous of all the wading tribes, there being no less than ninety-six different species enumerated by late writers. These are again subdivided into particular families, each distinguished by a certain peculiarity. The Cranes, by having the head bald; the Storks, with the orbits naked; and the Herons, with the middle claw pectinated. To this last belong the Bitterns. Several of these are nocturnal birds, feeding only as the evening twilight commences, and reposing either among the long grass and reeds, or on tall trees, in sequestered places, during the day. What is very remarkable, those night wanderers often associate, during the breeding season, with the others; building their nests on the branches of the same tree; and, though differing so little in external form, feeding on nearly the same food, living and lodging in the same place; yet preserve their race, language, and manners as perfectly distinct from those of their neighbours, as if each inhabited a separate quarter of the globe.

HUDSONIAN GODWIT.

SCOLOPAX HUDSONIA.

This beautiful shore bird, is for the first time pictured and presented to the public, through the "Cabinet of Natural History and American Rural Sports;" and the editor is much indebted to the Philadelphia Museum for this valuable acquisition to the ornithology of North America. It is a rare bird, being the only one of that species in the collection of the Museum, and as represented in the plate, is clothed in summer plumage. The only notice of this bird by former writers, is found in the supplementary part of Pennant's Arctic Zoology, and appears to have been communicated for publication there by the celebrated ornithologist Latham. The editor of this work has accordingly adopted the name for the bird supplied by that author.

HUDSONIAN GODWIT

BLUE CRANE

99

The chief abode and places of incubation for this bird appear to be Hudson's Bay and other northerly regions; as we have no notice of its being met with further south than Cape May, where the bird from which the present drawing is made was shot, in May, 1828, by Mr. Titian R. Peale. From thence north it is sometimes, though not frequently seen, and if seen, not known, and appears as fond of wandering along the shores of fresh water ponds as the sea side; it is social in its disposition; being met with in company with the Golden Plover. They usually appear in small parties of four or five; are not shy at first, but unsuspicious and easily shot, but it is seldom met with in the above plumage, which so differs from its fall or winter dress, that none but an experienced eye could identify the bird as the same when found in the latter plumage. From this circumstance I am inclined to think it much more common than is supposed; but not having appeared south, it has been unnoticed by Wilson and others, and thus omitted in the respective works on American Ornithology.

Mr. I. F. Ward, a naturalist of New York, who collects quantities of birds from different parts of the United States, for public and private cabinets, informs me, that he scarcely ever met with the Hudsonian Godwit, except on Hempstead Plains on Long Island, and then rarely dressed in the above plumage.

AMERICAN BUFFALO OR BISON.

BOS AMERICANUS.

Bos Americanus: Gmel. *Taurus Mexicanus:* Hernand. *Mex.* 587. *Tauri Vaccæque, Ibid. Anim. p.* 10. *The Buffalo:* Catesby, *Carol.* 28 *tab.* 20. *Bœuf Sauvage:* Dupratz, *Louisiane,* ii. 66. *American Bull:* Penn. *Quad. pl.* ii. *fig.* 2.

The physiognomy of the Bison is menacing and ferocious, and no one can see this formidable animal in his native wilds, for the first time, without feeling inclined to attend immediately to his personal safety. The summer coat of the Bison differs from his winter dress, rather by difference of length than by other particulars. In summer, from the shoulders backwards, the hinder parts of the animal are all covered with a very short fine hair, that is as smooth and as soft to the touch as velvet. The tail is quite short and tufted at the end, and its utility as a fly-brush is necessarily very limited. The colour of the hair is uniformly dun, but the long hair on the anterior parts of the body is to a certain extent tinged with yellowish or rust colour. These animals, however, present so little variety in regard to colour, that the natives consider any remarkable difference from the common appearance as resulting from the immediate interference of the Great Spirit.

From the dried flesh of the Bison the fur traders of the north-west prepare a food which is very valuable on account of the time it may be preserved without spoiling, though it will not appear very alluring to those who reside where provisions are obtained without difficulty. The dried Bison's flesh is placed on skins and pounded with stones until sufficiently pulverized. It is then separated as much as possible from impurities, and one-third of its weight of the melted tallow of the animal is poured over it. This substance is called *pemmican*, and being packed firmly in bags of skin of a convenient size for transportation, may be kept for one year without much difficulty, and with great care, perhaps two years.

The sense of smelling is remarkably acute in this animal, and it is remarked by hunters that the odour of the white man is far more terrifying to them than that of the Indian.

As an exemplification of the peculiar strength of their sense of smelling, we may here relate a circumstance mentioned by Mr. Say, in that valuable and highly interesting work, Long's Expedition to the Rocky Mountains, to which we are under continual obligations. These we are the more happy to acknowledge, because we are well acquainted with the solicitude of the gentlemen composing that expedition, to diffuse, as widely as possible, the knowledge of American Natural History.

The exploring party were riding through a dreary and uninteresting country, which at that time was enlivened by vast numbers of Bisons, who were moving in countless thousands in every direction. As the wind was blowing fresh from the south, the scent of the party was wafted directly across the river Platte, and through a distance of eight or ten miles, every step of its progress was distinctly marked by the terror and consternation it produced among the Bisons. The instant their atmosphere was infected by the tainted gale, they ran as violently as if closely pursued by mounted hunters, and instead of fleeing from the danger, they turned their heads towards the wind, eager to escape this terrifying odour. They dashed obliquely forward towards the party, and, plunging into the river, swam, waded, and ran with headlong violence, in several instances breaking through the Expedition's line of march, which was immediately along the left branch of the Platte. One of the party, (Mr. Say himself,) perceiving from the direction taken by the bull who led the extended column, that he would emerge from the low river bottom at a point where the precipitous bank was deeply worn by much travelling, urged his horse rapidly forward, that he might reach this station in order to gain a nearer view of these interesting animals. He had just reached the spot when the formidable leader, bounding up the steep, gained the summit of the bank with his fore feet, and in this position, suddenly halted from his full career, and fiercely glared at the horse which stood full in his path. The horse was panic-struck by this sudden apparition, trembled violently from fear, and would have wheeled and taken to flight, had not his rider exerted his utmost strength to restrain him; he recoiled, however, a few feet and sunk down upon his hams. The Bison halted for a moment, but urged forward by the irresistible pressure of the moving column behind, he rushed onward by the half-sitting horse. The herd then came swiftly on, crowding up the narrow defile. The party had now reached the spot, and extended along a considerable distance; the Bisons ran in a confused manner, in various directions, to gain the distant bluffs, and numbers were compelled to pass through the line of march. This scene, added to the plunging and roaring of those who were yet crossing the river, produced a grand effect, that was heightened by the fire opened on them by the hunters.

To the Indians and visitors of the western regions the Bison is almost invaluable; we have mentioned that they supply a large part of the food used by the natives, and covering to their tents and persons, while in many parts

AMERICAN BUFFALOE

Griffon Vulture.

of the country there is no fuel to be obtained but the dried dung of this animal. The Indians always associate ideas of enjoyment with plenty of Bison, and they frequently constitute the skull of one of them, their "Great Medicine." They have dances and ceremonies that are observed previous to the commencement of their hunting.

The herds of Bison wander over the country in search of food, usually led by a bull most remarkable for strength and fierceness. While feeding, they are often scattered over a great extent of country, but when they move in mass they form a dense almost impenetrable column, which, once in motion, is scarcely to be impeded. Their line of march is seldom interrupted even by considerable rivers, across which they swim without fear or hesitation, nearly in the order that they traverse the plains. When flying before their pursuers, it would be in vain for the foremost to halt, or attempt to obstruct the progress of the main body, as the throng in the rear still rushing onward, the leaders must advance, although destruction awaits the movement. The Indians take advantage of this circumstance to destroy great quantities of this favourite game,

and, certainly, no mode could be resorted to more effectually destructive, nor could a more terrible devastation be produced, than that of forcing a numerous herd of these large animals, to leap together from the brink of a dreadful precipice, upon a rocky and broken surface, a hundred feet below.

A better and more common way of killing Bison is that of attacking them on horseback. The Indians, mounted and well armed with bows and arrows, encircle the herd and gradually drive them into a situation favourable to the employment of the horse. They then ride in and single out one, generally a female, and following her as closely as possible, wound her with arrows until the mortal blow is given, when they go in pursuit of others until their quivers are exhausted. Should a wounded Bison attack the hunter, he escapes by the agility of his horse, which is usually well trained for the purpose. In some parts of the country, the hunter is exposed to a considerable danger of falling, in consequence of the numerous holes made in the plains by the badger.

SKUNK.

MEPHITIS AMERICANA.

Mephitis Americana; Desm. Godman *Vol.* I. *p.* 213,
  Viverra Mephitis; Gmel. [*L.*] *Syst. Nat. p.* 88, *No.*
  13, *Chinche;* Buff. *Hist. Nat. tom.* 33, *pl.* xx. *fig.*
  2. *Enfant du diable;* Charlev. *Nouv. France* v.
  196. *Skunk Weesel,* Penn. *Quad.* 2, *p.* 65, *No.* 263.

THE Skunk is a pretty and at the same time a most
noxious animal, and is ranked among those vermin so destructive to the farmers' interests, and to various descriptions of game.

Most persons are acquainted with this animal by character, although but few know it by sight; nor do any seek to
encounter it farther than with feelings of enmity or revenge, as it is an unwelcome visiter to any neighbourhood,
in consequence of its destructive and other disagreeable
habits. When its abode is well secured it is a most difficult matter to dislodge or drive it from the premises; and
there is perhaps no animal possessing so little energy and
strength, which is so completely protected by other natural means from its enemies.

The fetor emitted by the Skunk, when defending itself,
is so exceedingly powerful, as will almost suffocate its antagonist and cause a rapid retreat from so disgusting an
enemy. This stench can be produced or retained at pleasure by the animal, and is seldom diffused, except when
violence is committed toward it, or in defending itself
from attack.

The Skunk, like most predatory animals, seldom travels
in the day time, but so soon as twilight of the evening has
approached, it sallies forth in search of prey, and while
the unsuspicious and innocent objects of its search are
sleeping, they become the easy victims to the rapacity of
this destroyer. The Skunk destroys its prey almost instantly. This is in consequence of the suddenness with
which it strikes the intended victim at the throat, and the
sharpness of its teeth and strength of grasp produces death
so soon, and with so much quietness, that even in a hen-
roost no alarm is given to a neighbouring fowl by the intruder, or the unfortunate sufferer. With, however, its
destructive habits, it has some redeeming qualities, as it
is a great enemy to rats, and will utterly destroy these
vermin, as readily as the ferret; and it is said that some
farmers on this account encourage their presence by all

possible protection; and a certain author states, that " he
witnessed an instance where a great number of rats were
found in a stack of wheat, but all of them in the upper
part; for several yards from the ground, not a rat was to
be met with, which excited some surprise; but the circumstance was fully explained on reaching the bottom,
where it was found an enormous Skunk had taken up its
abode."

This animal is very common throughout the United
States, but, as it roams only during the night season, it is
seldom seen, except by accident. The writer, during his
residence at the paternal home, a few miles from this city,
frequently encountered the Skunk, and became in a measure familiarized to its disgusting habits: to a person, however, ignorant of the animal and the stench it produces,
the scent for the first time is exceedingly offensive and intolerable, and the most credulous would not believe its
power, until it could be sensibly experienced. In one
instance, while hunting woodcock during the month of
August, one of my dogs encountered and killed a Skunk
before I could approach the belligerents, and from the effects of the fetor received in the battle, he was rendered
entirely useless for a whole year, and did not recover the
goodness of his nose for nearly double that time. Subsequently I was hunting with the same dog after partridges,
and while passing through a large wood, he came to a
stand near a pile of cleft wood: thinking a rabbit had
taken shelter beneath it, I endeavoured in vain to dislodge
it; at length, stooping down to take a closer survey, I
discovered a Skunk sitting in a defensive posture, ready
in a moment to discharge its powerful artillery; wishing
to have a joke with a gentleman who was with me, and
who was entirely ignorant of the animal in question, I requested him to approach and examine the stranger, to
which he assented; and after expressing his admiration,
and made some inquiries about it, I told him to stand where
he was until I shot it. Not suspecting my design, he approached to within five or six feet, while I receded as
many yards and shot the animal. Immediately my friend
was enveloped in this horrible stench, almost to suffoca-
tion, who retreated fifty or sixty yards, coughing and puff-
ing so vehemently, as caused me to regret that I had played
the trick on his ignorance. The volatility of this odour
is wonderful, and can be scented at a great distance. In
the above instance, the animal was killed nearly three-
fourths of a mile from our destined home, and ere we
reached it, the inmates of the house had experienced the
scent, and asked us on our arrival, if we had not killed a
Skunk.

FLICKER,
OR GOLDEN-WINGED WOODPECKER.

PICUS AURATUS.

[on a branch of Sour Gum.]

Le Pic aux ailes dorées, Buffon, vii. 39. *Pl. Enl.*
693.—*Picus auratus*, Linn. *Syst.* 174.—*Cuculus
alis de auratis*, Klein, *p.* 30.—Catesby, i. 18.—Latham, ii. 597.—Bartram, *p.* 289.—*Cuculus auratus*,
Linn. *Syst. ed.* 10, 1, 112.—Gmel. *Syst.* i. 430.—
Lath. *Ind. Orn. p.* 242.—*Picus Canadensis striatus*,
Briss. iv. 72.—Penn. *Arct. Zool. No.* 158.—J. Doughty's Collection.

This elegant bird is well known to our farmers and junior sportsmen, who take every opportunity of destroying him; the former for the supposed trespasses he commits on their Indian corn, or the trifle he will bring in
market, and the latter for the mere pleasure of destruction, and perhaps for the flavour of his flesh, which is in
general esteem.

The food of this bird varies with the season. As the
common cherries, bird-cherries, and berries of the sour
gum, successively ripen, he regales plentifully on them,
particularly on the latter; but the chief food of this species, or that which is most usually found in his stomach,
is wood-lice, and the young and larvæ of ants, of which
he is so immoderately fond, that I have frequently found
his stomach distended with a mass of these, and these only,
as large nearly as a plum. For the procuring of these insects, nature has remarkably fitted him. The bills of
Woodpeckers, in general, are straight, grooved or chan-
nelled, wedge-shaped, and compressed to a thin edge at
the end, that they may the easier penetrate the hardest
wood; that of the Golden-winged Woodpecker is long,
slightly bent, ridged only on the top, and tapering almost
to a point, yet still retaining a little of the wedge form
there. Both, however, are admirably adapted to the peculiar manner each has of procuring its food. The former, like a powerful wedge, to penetrate the dead and decaying branches, after worms and insects; the latter, like
a long and sharp pick-axe, to dig up the hillocks of pis-
mires, that inhabit old stumps in prodigious multitudes.
These beneficial services would entitle him to some regard from the husbandman, were he not accused, and
perhaps not without just cause, of being too partial to the
Indian corn, when in that state which is usually called
roasting-ears. His visits are indeed rather frequent
about this time; and the farmer, suspecting what is going
on, steals through among the rows with his gun, bent on

vengeance, and forgetful of the benevolent sentiment of
the poet;—that

> "———— Just as wide of *justice* he must fall
> Who thinks all made for One, not one for all."

But farmers, in general, are not much versed in poetry,
and pretty well acquainted with the value of corn, from
the hard labour requisite in raising it.

In rambling through the woods one day, I happened to
shoot at one of these birds, and wounded him slightly in
the wing. Finding him in full feather, and seemingly
but little hurt, I took him home, and put him into a large
cage, made of willows, intending to keep him in my own
room, that we might become better acquainted. As soon
as he found himself inclosed on all sides, he lost no time
in idle fluttering, but throwing himself against the bars of
the cage, began instantly to demolish the willows, batter-
ing them with great vehemence, and uttering a loud piteous kind of cackling, similar to that of a hen when she is
alarmed, and takes to wing. Poor Baron Trenck never
laboured with more eager diligence at the walls of his
prison, than this son of the forest in his exertions for
liberty; and he exercised his powerful bill with such force,
digging into the sticks, seizing and shaking them so from
side to side, that he soon opened for himself a passage;
and though I repeatedly repaired the breach, and barri-
cadoed every opening in the best manner I could, yet on
my return into the room, I always found him at large,
climbing up the chairs, or running about the floor, where,
from the dexterity of his motions, moving backwards,
forwards, and sideways, with the same facility, it became
difficult to get hold of him again. Having placed him in
a strong wire cage, he seemed to give up all hopes of
making his escape, and soon became very tame; fed on
young ears of Indian corn; refused apples, but ate the
berries of the sour gum greedily, small winter grapes, and
several other kinds of berries; exercised himself frequently in climbing, or rather hopping perpendicularly along
the sides of the cage; and as evening drew on, fixed himself in a high hanging or perpendicular position, and slept
with his head in his wing. As soon as dawn appeared,
even before it was light enough to perceive him distinctly across the room, he descended to the bottom of the
cage, and began his attack on the ears of Indian corn, rap-
ping so loud as to be heard from every room in the house.
After this he would sometimes resume his former position,
and take another nap. He was beginning to become very
amusing, and even sociable, when, after a lapse of several
weeks, he became drooping, and died, as I conceived, from
the effects of his wound.

FLICKER, OR GOLDEN-WINGED WOODPECKER

GANNET
(ADULT)

GANNET
(YOUNG)

110

THE GANNET.

PELECANUS BASSANUS.
[Young and adult.]

Pelecanus Bassanus, LINN. *Syst.* 217. *Anser Bassanus,* GESNER *av.* 163. *Solan Goose* WIL. *Orn.* 328. RAII. *Syn. av.* 122, *Martins Voy. St. Kilda,* 27, *Descript. West. Isles,* 281. *Sula Bassana le Fou de Bassan* BRISSON *av.* VI. 503, *tab.* 44. *Jaen. Van Gent. Martin's Spitsberg,* 97. *Sula. Horeri Cluf. ex* 367, *Hector Boeth.* 6. *Norvegis Sule, Hav.—Sul.* BRUNNICH, 124, *Pennant, British Zool. Vol.* 2. *p.* 518, *Pl.* 103, *White's Ed.*—J. DOUGHTY's Collection.

THE Gannet, although a frequent visiter of our seashore, has thus far been unnoticed in American works on ornithology. It is now for the first time pictured in the accompanying plate, and is represented in the young and adult stages of existence. The young Gannet was for a long time mistaken, and described by some naturalists as another species, but lately these errors have been corrected.

The Gannet is strong on the wing, especially in windy weather, and is seldom seen inside of the surf, but is mostly sailing over the waters, in order to discover and strike its prey. This bird is very awkward on foot, in consequence of the shortness of the legs and their position; being placed far behind, which necessarily causes the bird to walk nearly upright, like the corvorant; the tail, which extends beyond the feet, is always ragged or worn at the end, by being dragged on the ground by the bird when walking on the beach. For a more ample history and description of the Gannet, the following is selected from Pennant's British Zoology.

"This species weighs seven pounds: the length is three feet one inch; the breadth six feet two inches. The bill is six inches long, straight almost to the point, where it inclines down; and the sides are irregularly jagged, that it may hold its prey with more security: about an inch from the base of the upper mandible is a sharp process pointing forward; it has no nostrils; but in their place a long furrow, that reaches almost to the end of the bill: the whole is of a dirty white, tinged with ash colour. The tongue is very small, and placed low in the mouth: a naked skin of a fine blue surrounds the eyes, which are of a pale yellow, and are full of vivacity: this bird is remarkable for the quickness of its sight: Martin tells us that Solan is derived from an Irish word expressive of that quality.

"From the corner of the mouth is a narrow slip of black bare skin, that extends to the hind part of the head: beneath the chin is another, that like the pouch of the *Pelecan,* is dilatable, and of size sufficient to contain five or six entire herrings; which, in the breeding season, it carries at once to its mate or young.

"The neck is very long: the body flat, and very full of feathers: the crown of the head, and a small space on the hind part of the neck is buff coloured: the rest of the plumage is white, the bastard wing and greater quill-feather excepted, which are black; the legs and toes are black; but the fore part of both are marked with a stripe of fine pea green. The tail consists of twelve sharp pointed feathers, the middle of which is the longest.

"The young birds, during the first year, differ greatly in colour from the old ones; being of a dusky hue, speckled with numerous triangular white spots; and at that time resemble in colours the speckled Diver. Each bird, if left undisturbed, would only lay one egg in the year; but if that be taken away, they will lay another; if that is also taken, then a third; but never more that season: a wise provision of nature, to prevent the extinction of the species by accidents, and to supply food for the inhabitants of the places where they breed. Their egg is white, and rather less than that of the common goose: the nest is large, and formed of any thing the bird finds floating on the water, such as grass, sea plants, shavings, &c. These birds frequent the Isle of Ailsa, in the Firth of Clyde; the rocks adjacent to St. Kilda, the Stack of Souliskery, near the Orkneys; the Skelig Isles, off the coasts of Kerry Ireland, and the Bass Isle, in the Firth of Edinburgh: the multitudes that inhabit these places are prodigious. Dr. Harvey's elegant account of the latter, will serve to give some idea of the numbers of these, and of the other birds that annually migrate to that little spot.

"There is a small island, called by the Scotch, Bass Island, not more than a mile in circumference; the surface is almost wholly covered during the months of May and June with nests, eggs, and young birds; so that it is scarcely possible to walk without treading on them: and the flocks of birds in flight are so prodigious, as to darken the air like clouds; and their noise is such, that you cannot, without difficulty, hear your next neighbour's voice. If you look down upon the sea, from the top of the precipice, you will see it on every side covered with infinite numbers of birds of different kinds, swimming and hunting for their prey: if in sailing round the island you survey the hanging cliffs, you may see in every crag or fissure of the broken rocks, innumerable birds of various sorts and sizes, more than the stars of heaven when viewed in a serene night: if from afar you see the distant flocks, either flying to or from the island, you would imagine them to be a vast swarm of bees."

POLAR BEAR.

URSUS MARITIMUS.

Ursus Maritimus, Linn. *Ursus Albus.* Briss. *Règne Anim. p.* 260. *sp.* 2. *Ours Blanc;* Buff. *Supp. tom.* 3. *pl.*34. *Ours Blanc:* Desm. *Mam. p.* 16. *sp.* 257. *The Polar Bear:* Penn. *Syn. quad. p.* 192. *tab.* 20. *fig.* 1. Pallas, *spicil. Zool.* xiv. *tab.* 1.—Menagerie Living Animals, exhibited in Philadelphia, winter of 1832—3.

In the desolate regions of the north, where unrelenting winter reigns in full appanage of horrors during the greater part of the year, and even the stormy ocean itself is long imprisoned by "thick ribbed ice," the Polar Bear finds his most congenial abode. There, prowling over the frozen wastes, he satiates his hunger on the carcasses of whales deserted by the adventurous fishermen, or seizes on such marine animals as come up to bask in open air; and when occasion calls, he fearlessly plunges into the sea in pursuit of his prey, as if the deep were his native and familiar element. To most other animals extreme cold is distressing and injurious; to him it is welcome and delightful: to him the glistening ice-bank or snow-wreathed shore, canopied by louring and tempestuous clouds, are far more inviting and agreeable, than verdant hills or sunny skies.

Being endowed with extremely acute senses, great strength, and a savagely ferocious disposition withal, it is not surprising that this animal is dreaded as the most formidable quadruped of the region he inhabits. Notwithstanding his great size and apparent heaviness, he is very active, and though his ordinary gait may appear clumsy, when excited by rage or hunger, his speed on the ice far exceeds that of the swiftest man.

When on an extensive ice-field, the Polar Bear is often observed to ascend the knobs or hummocks, for the purpose of reconnoitering, or he stands with head erect to snuff the tainted air, which informs him where to find the whale carrion at astonishing distances. This substance, so unpleasant and disgusting to human sense, is a luxurious banquet to the bear, and a piece of it thrown on a fire will allure him from a distance of several miles.

A considerable part of the Polar Bear's food is supplied by seals, but very probably he suffers long fasts and extreme hunger, owing to the peculiar vigilance of these creatures; occasionally he is much reduced by being carried out to sea on a small island of ice, where he may be forced to remain for a week or more without an opportunity of procuring food. In this situation they have been seen on ice-islands two hundred miles distant from land, and sometimes they are drifted to the shores of Iceland, or Norway, where they are so ravenous as to destroy all the animals they find. Most commonly such invaders are soon destroyed, as the natives collect in large numbers and commence an immediate pursuit, but frequently do not succeed in killing them, before many of their flocks are thinned. An individual Polar Bear has occasionally been carried on the ice as far south as Newfoundland, but this circumstance very rarely occurs.

This animal swims excellently, and advances at the rate of three miles an hour. During the summer season he principally resides on the ice-islands, and leaves one to visit another, however great be the distance. If interrupted while in the water, he dives and changes his course; but he neither dives very often, nor does he remain under water for a long time. Captain Ross saw a Polar Bear swimming midway in Melville Sound, where the shores were full forty miles apart, and no ice was in sight large enough for him to have rested on. The best time for attacking him is when he is in the water; on ice or land he has so many advantages that the aggressor is always in danger. Even in the water he has frequently proved a formidable antagonist, has boarded and taken possession of a small boat, forcing the occupants to seek safety by leaping overboard. Instances are related in which this animal has climbed up the sides of small vessels, and been with difficulty repelled from the deck.

Generally the Polar Bear retreats from man; but when pursued and attacked he always resents the aggression, and turns furiously on his enemy. When struck at with a lance, he is very apt to seize and bite the staff in two, or wrest it from the hands. Should a ball be fired at him, without taking effect in the head or heart, his rage is increased, and he seeks revenge with augmented fury. It has been remarked that, when wounded and able to make his escape, he applies snow to the wound, as if aware that cold would check the flow of blood.

The female Polar Bear is as rugged in her appearance, and as savagely ferocious in disposition, as her mate; yet to her offspring she displays a tenderness of affection which strongly contrasts with her fierce and sanguinary temper. When her cubs are exposed, danger has no existence to her, and nothing but death can compel her to desist from struggling desperately to defend or save them. The death of her offspring is with great difficulty acknowledged by the parent; when they are shot by her side the poor beast solicits their attention by every fond artifice, and endeavours to awaken them from their unnatural

POLAR BEAR

sleep: she offers them food, licks their wounds, caresses and moans over them in such a manner as to evince a degree of feeling which could scarcely be anticipated from so rude and terrible a quadruped.

Numerous instances of this fondness of attachment have been observed, and some of them attended with most singular displays of sagacity on the part of the mother. The following circumstance is related in Scoresby's account of the Arctic Regions, and is entitled to the fullest credence, because coming from so competent and excellent an observer:

"A she-bear, with her two cubs, were pursued on the ice by some of the men, and were so closely approached, as to alarm the mother for the safety of her offspring. Finding that they could not advance with the desired speed, she used various artifices to urge them forward, but without success. Determined to save them, if possible, she ran to one of the cubs, placed her nose under it, and threw it forward as far as possible; then going to the other, she performed the same action, and repeated it frequently until she had thus conveyed them to a considerable distance. The young bears seemed perfectly conscious of their mother's intention, for as soon as they recovered their feet, after being thrown forward, they immediately ran on in the proper direction, and when the mother came up to renew the effort, the little rogues uniformly placed themselves across her path, that they might receive the full advantage of the force exerted for their safety."

The most affecting instance on record of the maternal affection exhibited by this bear, is related in one of the Polar Voyages; it conveys so excellent an idea of this creature's strong feeling of parental love, that we should deem the history of the animal imperfect, were such an illustration omitted.

"Early in the morning, the man at the mast-head gave notice that three bears were making their way very fast over the ice, and directing their course towards the ship. They had probably been invited by the blubber of a sea-horse, which the men had set on fire, and which was burning on the ice at the time of their approach. They proved to be a she-bear and her two cubs; but the cubs were nearly as large as the dam. They ran eagerly to the fire, and drew out from the flames part of the flesh of the sea-horse, which remained unconsumed, and ate it voraciously. The crew from the ship threw great pieces of the flesh, which they had still left, upon the ice, which the old bear carried away singly, laid every piece before her cubs, and dividing them, gave each a share, reserving but a small portion to herself. As she was carrying away the last piece, they levelled their muskets at the cubs,

and shot them both dead; and in her retreat, they wounded the dam, but not mortally.

"It would have drawn tears of pity from any but unfeeling minds, to have marked the affectionate concern manifested by this poor beast, in the last moments of her expiring young. Though she was sorely wounded, and could but just crawl to the place where they lay, she carried the lump of flesh she had fetched away, as she had done the others before, tore it in pieces, and laid it down before them; and when she saw they refused to eat, she laid her paws first upon one, and then upon the other, and endeavoured to raise them up. All this while it was piteous to hear her moan. When she found she could not stir them, she went off; and when at some distance, looked back and moaned; and that not availing to entice them away, she returned, and smelling around them, began to lick their wounds. She went off a second time, as before; and having crawled a few paces looked again behind her, and for some time stood moaning. But still her cubs not rising to follow her, she returned to them again, and with signs of inexpressible fondness, went round first one and then the other, pawing them, and moaning. Finding at last that they were cold and lifeless, she raised her head towards the ship, and growled her resentment at the murderers; which they returned with a volley of musket balls. She fell between her cubs, and died licking their wounds."

The sagacity of the Polar Bear is well known to the whale fishers, who often find all their ingenuity insufficient to entrap him, as the following instance may serve to show. A noose, baited with a piece of "kreng," or whale carcass, was placed at a proper distance from the ship, which soon attracted the attention of a large bear. In attempting to secure the bait, the animal by some movement drew the noose, so as to catch him by one of his fore-paws. Apparently unconcerned by this circumstance, and conscious of knowing how to free himself from restraint, he quietly loosened the slip-knot with the other paw, and leisurely walked off to enjoy his morsel. The trap was again baited, and the bear once more approached to obtain his favourite food, but, grown wise by experience, he carefully avoided the rope, and carried off the bait, to the mortification of the captain, who wished to obtain his skin. The whaler, resolved to baffle the address of the bear, re-arranged his noose once more, carefully burying the rope at a considerable depth in the snow: but his precautions were unavailing; the bear cautiously examined the vicinity, scented the ground with attention, detected the situation of the rope, dug it up and threw it out of his way; then securing his prize, he once more triumphantly withdrew to enjoy it.

SNIPE

SNIPE.

SCOLOPAX GALLINAGO.

[J. Doughty's Collection.]

THIS bird is well known to our sportsmen; and, if not the same, has a very near resemblance of the common Snipe of Europe. It is usually known by the name of the *English Snipe*, to distinguish it from the woodcock, and from several others of the same genus. It arrives in Pennsylvania about the 10th of March, and remains in the low grounds for several weeks; the greater part then move off to the north, and to the higher inland districts to breed. A few are occasionally found, and consequently breed in our low marshes during the summer. When they first arrive, they are usually lean; but when in good order are accounted excellent eating. They are, perhaps, the most difficult to shoot of all our birds, as they fly in sudden zig-zag lines, and very rapidly. Great numbers of these birds winter in the rice grounds of the southern states, where, in the month of February, they appeared to be much tamer than they are usually here, as I frequently observed them running about among the springs and watery thickets. I was told by the inhabitants, that they generally disappeared early in the spring. On the 20th of March I found these birds extremely numerous on the borders of the ponds near Louisville, Kentucky; and also in the neighbourhood of Lexington, in the same state, as late as the 10th of April. I was told by several people, that they are abundant in the Illinois country, up as far as Lake Michigan. They are but seldom seen in Pennsylvania during the summer, but are occasionally met with in considerable numbers on their return in autumn, along the whole eastern side of the Alleghany, from the sea to the mountains. They have the same soaring irregular flight in the air in gloomy weather as the Snipe of Europe; the same bleating note, and occasional rapid descent; spring from the marshes with the like feeble *squeak;* and in every respect resemble the common Snipe of Britain, except in being about an inch less; and in having sixteen feathers in the tail instead of fourteen, the number said by Bewick to be in that of Europe. From these circumstances, we must either conclude this to be a different species, or partially changed by difference of climate; the former appears to me the more probable opinion of the two.

These birds abound in the meadows, and low grounds, along our large rivers, particularly those that border the Schuylkill and Delaware, from the 10th of March to the middle of April, and sometimes later, and are eagerly sought after by many of our gunners. The nature of the grounds, however, which these birds frequent, the coldness of the season, and peculiar shyness and agility of the game, render this amusement attractive only to the most dexterous, active, and eager of our sportsmen.

GREY SQUIRREL

THE GRAY SQUIRREL.

SCIURUS CAROLINENSIS.

Sciurus Carolinensis et Cinereus; Gmel. Schreb. *tab.* 213. *Sciurus Carolinensis,* Godman. *Vol.* 2. *p.* 131. *Petit Gris:* Buff. 10. *pl.* 25. *encycl. pl.* 74. *fig.* 3. *Ecureuil gris de la Carolina;* Bosc. ii. *p.* 96. *pl.* 29: F. Cuv. *Mam. Lithog. livr.* 11e. *Gray Squirrel:* Penn. *Arct. Zool.* i. 135. *Hist. Quad. No.* 272.—J. Doughty's Collection.

There are few animals better known in this country than the one under present notice, and, from the circumstance of their being introduced so frequently as pets in human habitations, our knowledge is acquired at a very early age. They are, however, so plentifully scattered over every part of the United States, that it is to be presumed, scarcely an individual can be found who is ignorant of the Gray Squirrel.

The pursuit of this animal has always been looked upon as a very inviting sport, and is entered into by both old and young, until age and eyesight in the former render the sport a burthen; and by the latter, so soon as the fowling-piece or rifle can be effectually wielded, and "dropping Squirrels" from the tallest trees, are the boasted exploits of each. On the mountains, and in the newly-settled districts of the country, this sport is very common; perhaps because these animals abound in greater numbers there. In destroying Squirrels some use the short gun, and others the rifle; the latter, however, is more commonly used, in consequence of the good practice the sport affords for the use of that instrument; the part usually aimed at is the head, and so accurate are practitioners in shooting the rifle, that seldom any other part of the animal is struck; sometimes, those who are superior in skill, show their dexterity in killing the animal, without striking it with the ball; this is called by the hunters "barking Squirrels," and is performed by striking the bark immediately under the Squirrel, which destroys life instantaneously, by the violence of the concussion thus effected.

To an inexperienced eye, the Squirrel, when lodged in the foliage of a tall tree, is a difficult object to discover, and when seen by such, they frequently are at a loss to determine whether the object seen is a Squirrel or not.

These animals are not only shy, but most agile in their movements, and these qualities are increased accordingly as they become persecuted, to so great extent, that in passing from limb to limb of adjoining trees, they frequently elude the most active pursuit.

In districts where Squirrels abound, they may be seen at all hours, except the middle of the day; but in thickly inhabited neighbourhoods, where they are shot at and worried much, it requires great caution to discover them; the most propitious periods then, are from daylight to sunrise, and from sunset until dark. The approach of the huntsman at these times must be with much quietness and caution, and must be directed always to those trees which are their favourite resort for food, the chief of which is the shellbark. The keen eye of an experienced Squirrel hunter cannot always discover the object of his pursuit on the tall trees which grow in our forests, and is often obliged to determine the presence of these animals by the fragments gnawed from the nuts which lie scattered beneath the trees. Sometimes a dropping nut denotes a Squirrel nigh, if not on the tree of his immediate search. A falling nut may be heard through the still wood at a very considerable distance, and so soon as the sound reaches the ear of the hunter, he directs his footsteps to the spot whence the sound proceeded, with quiet stealth, and soon discovers the game eating its food on the topmost branches of the tree; sometimes the animal, warned of the approach of its enemy by the rustling leaves or the cracking twigs beneath his footsteps, seeks safety by escaping to its hole, or hides itself against some large limb of the same tree, or runs to the extremity of the top, and there remains motionless in supposed security amid the thickest collection of leaves. The eyes and ingenuity of the hunter are now employed to detect his prey; he looks with intensity into every limb and branch, but unable to discern the wary little animal, he tries other positions around the tree, until at length he sees a spot among the leaves of more density than other parts, or perhaps, on a limb, a small gray tuft, like moss or tow, and levelling his gun, he fires, and the falling Squirrel proves the unerring certainty of his judgment. It often happens, however, that a Squirrel cannot be discovered in these positions when in a quiescent state, and ingenuity is employed to excite motion, and this effected, no matter how trivial, will at once discover the position of the game. The means usually employed to do this, are the shaking of a small bush near or under the tree on which the animal is supposed to be lodged, or striking its trunk with violence.

PURPLE FINCH

PINE FINCH

PURPLE FINCH.

FRINGILLA PURPUREA.

[on a branch of Sycamore.]

Fringilla Purpurea, GMEL. *Syst.* I. 923.—*Bouvreuil violet de la Caroline*, BUFF. IV. 395.—*Purple Finch, Arct. Zool.* II. No. 258.—CATESB. I. 41.—LATH. *Syn.* III. 275, 39.—*Crimson-headed Finch, Arct. Zool.* II. No. 257.—LATHAM, *Syn.* III. 275, 39.—*Hemp-bird*, BARTRAM, 291—*Fringilla Purpurea, Id.* 291.—J. DOUGHTY's Collection.

THIS is a winter bird of passage, coming to us in large flocks from the north, in September and October, great numbers remaining with us in Pennsylvania during the whole winter, feeding on the seeds of the poplar, button-wood, juniper, cedar; and on those of many rank weeds that flourish in rich bottoms, and along the margin of creeks. When the season is very severe they proceed to the south, as far at least as Georgia, returning north early in April. They now frequent the elm trees, feeding on the slender but sweet covering of the flowers; and as soon as the cherries put out their blossoms, feed almost exclusively on the stamina of the flowers; afterwards the apple blossoms are attacked in the same manner; and their depredations on these continue till they disappear, which is usually about the 10th or middle of May. I have been told that they sometimes breed in the northern parts of New-York, but have never met with their nests. About the middle of September I found these birds numerous on Long Island, and round Newark, in New-Jersey. They fly at a considerable height in the air, and their note is a single *chink*, like that of the Rice-bird. They possess great boldness and spirit, and when caught, bite violently, and hang by the bill from your hand, striking with great fury; but they are soon reconciled to confinement, and in a day or two are quite at home. I have kept a pair of these birds upwards of nine months, to observe their manners. One was caught in a trap, the other was winged with the gun; both are now as familiar as if brought up from the nest by the hand, and seem to prefer hempseed and cherry blossoms to all other kinds of food. Both male and female, though not crested, are almost constantly in the habit of erecting the feathers of the crown; they appear to be of a tyrannical and domineering disposition, for they nearly killed an indigo-bird, and two or three others that were occasionally placed with them, driving them into a corner of the cage, standing on them and tearing out their feathers, striking them on the head, munching their wings, &c. &c., till I was obliged to interfere; and even if called to, the aggressor would only turn up a malicious eye to me for a moment, and renew his outrage as before. They are a hardy, vigorous bird. In the month of October, about the time of their first arrival, I shot a male, rich in plumage, and plump in flesh, but which wanted one leg, that had been taken off a little above the knee; the wound had healed so completely, and was covered with so thick a skin, that it seemed as though it had been so for years. Whether this mutilation was occasioned by a shot, or in party quarrels of its own, I could not determine; but our invalid seemed to have used his stump either in hopping or resting, for it had all the appearance of having been brought in frequent contact with other bodies harder than itself.

PINE FINCH.

FRINGILLA PINUS.

J. DOUGHTY's Collection.

THIS little northern stranger visits us in the month of November, and seeks the seeds of the black alder, on the borders of swamps, creeks and rivulets. As the weather becomes more severe, and the seeds of the *Pinus canadensis* are fully ripe, these birds collect in large flocks, and take up their residence, almost exclusively, among these trees. In the gardens of Bushhill, in the neighbourhood of Philadelphia, a flock of two or three hundred of these birds have regularly wintered many years; where a noble avenue of pine trees, and walks covered with fine white gravel, furnish them with abundance through the winter. Early in March they disappear, either to the north, or to the pine woods that cover many lesser ranges of the Alleghany. While here they are often so tame as to allow you to walk within a few yards of the spot where a whole flock of them are sitting. They flutter among the branches, frequently hanging by the cones, and uttering a note almost exactly like that of the goldfinch, (*F. tristis.*) I have not a doubt but this bird appears in a richer dress in summer in those places where he breeds as he has so very great a resemblance to the bird above mentioned, with whose changes we are well acquainted.

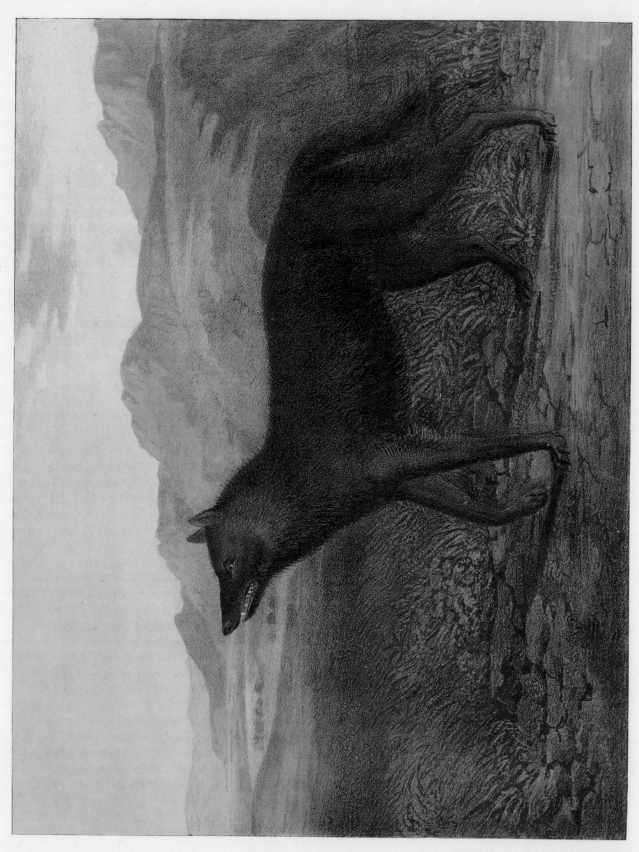

BLACK WOLF

THE BLACK WOLF.

CANIS NUBILUS.

Canis Lycaon; Linn. Shrel. *Saeugthiere, pl.* 89. Godman, *Vol.* 1. *p.* 267.—*Loup Noir;* Buff. 9. *pl.* 41.
Black Wolf: Say *in Long's Expedition to the Rocky
Mountains, p.* 102, *Vol.* 1.—Menagerie Living Animals exhibited in Philadelphia, winter of 1832—3.

There was, for some time, much doubt among naturalists, whether the Black Wolf should be considered a
separate species, or only a variety of the common Wolf;
but, on a close investigation of the internal and anatomical structure, habits and general appearance of the Black
Wolf, it has become a settled question that it is a different animal altogether. Of the two animals belonging to the
Zoological gardens of London, it is remarked, "that they
exhibit real and substantial marks of distinction of sufficient value to sanction their separation from the other
species—considerably longer and more robust than the
common Wolf, and differing greatly in the expression of
their physiognomy; neither in figure nor in countenance
are they remarkable for that starved and gaunt appearance which is the common and well known attribute of
the latter. In fact, they have altogether a more fierce and
formidable, but, at the same time, a more noble and less
sinister aspect.

"Their hair, which is of considerable length, especially along the middle of the back and shoulders, where it
forms an indistinct and scattered mane, is mottled with
various shades of black, gray and white, giving to the
whole animal that dark and clouded colour which constitutes one of its most peculiar and striking characteristics.
The colouring, which, on the upper parts of the body
is deep black, becomes somewhat lighter on the sides,
and assumes a yet brighter shade beneath: the chin and
angles of the mouth are nearly white; the gray tinge pre-
dominating over the darker shades in various other parts,
but by no means in so regular a manner as to merit a particular description. The ears are remarkably short, and
the tail is also somewhat shorter in proportion than that
of the common Wolf, not reaching in its solid form beneath the posterior bend (which, in all these animals, is
formed by the heel) of the hind legs."

These animals, it appears, were sent to England by the
Hudson's Bay Company, by some of whose hunters they
had been trapped in the northern regions of America.

They are represented as exceedingly voracious, tearing
their meat and swallowing it in large gobbets, and afterwards gnawing the bones with truly wolfish avidity.
"Their length is four feet and a quarter from the tip of
the nose to the origin of the tail."

Dr. Godman, in describing the Black Wolf, says: "in
general appearance and the relative proportions of the
different parts of the body, this Wolf resembles the common wolf, (Canis Lupas,) but in size it is intermediate to
the fox and common wolf. The colour of the animal is
its most remarkable characteristic: it is entirely black,
without the slightest admixture of any other colour."

Of these two descriptions of the Black Wolf, the writer considers the former the most correct, having, from
actual observation, closely noticed the structure, habits
and disposition of the animal, as far as a state of half do-
mesticity would permit.

The animal from which the drawing in the preceding
plate was taken, belongs to the celebrated Menagerie of
living animals, exhibited in various parts of this country
by Messrs. Welsh, Purdy & Co., and corresponds in most
particulars with those belonging to the Zoological gardens of London. Dr. Godman, however, may be correct,
(and I am inclined to think he is,) in regard to the colour
of the animal being perfectly black, as long confinement
and restraint on the natural habits of this Wolf, may have
great influence in changing the pelage or its colour.

The Black Wolf appears to be confined chiefly to the
Rocky Mountains, and the more northerly regions of
America; it is, perhaps, the rarest of its genus, and but
few specimens have ever been presented to public view,
although almost every district of North America is infested with the other species.

The animal under immediate notice was brought by
some traders, while yet a whelp, from the neighbourhood
of the Rocky Mountains, to one of the towns on the Missouri, from thence it found its way to the Menagerie spo-
ken of; but in consequence of much suffering by confinement, especially with the mange, it became necessary to
remove it from the company of the other wild animals.
This Wolf, although at times it evinced much ferocity,
would generally suffer the writer to pet it, and would frequently lie down and crouch like a dog, and utter the
same whining cry of humility; it was exceedingly active
and graceful in every motion, and when irritated, would
growl and snap with violence at any object intended to
worry it, and when punished, would yelp like a dog; he
was not gaunt, but fat, and very stately in his appearance,
moving about with head and tail very erect.

BELTED KING FISHER

BUFFEL HEADED DUCK

124

BELTED KINGSFISHER.

ALCEDO ALCYON.

BARTRAM, *p.* 289.—TURTON, *p.* 278.—*Alcedo Alcyon,* LINN. *Syst. ed.* 10, *vol.* I. 115.—GMEL. *Syst.* I. 451.— LATH. *Ind. Orn.* 257.—CATESBY, I. 60.—BUFF. *Pl. Enl.* 593—715.—J. DOUGHTY's Collection.

THIS is a general inhabitant of the banks and shores of all our fresh-water rivers, from Hudson's Bay to Mexico; and is the only species of its tribe found within the United States. This last circumstance, and its characteristic appearance, make it as universally known here, as its elegant little brother, the common Kingsfisher of Europe, is in Britain. Like the love-lorn swains, of whom poets tell us, he delights in murmuring streams and falling waters; not, however, merely that they may soothe his ear, but for a gratification more substantial. Amidst the roar of the cataract, or over the foam of a torrent, he sits perched upon an overhanging bough, glancing his piercing eye in every direction below for his scaly prey, which, with a sudden circular plunge, he sweeps from their native element, and swallows in an instant. His voice, which is not unlike the twirling of a watchman's rattle, is naturally loud, harsh, and sudden; but is softened by the sound of the brawling streams and cascades among which he generally rambles. He courses along the windings of the brook or river, at a small height above the surface, sometimes suspending himself by the rapid action of his wings, like certain species of hawks, ready to pounce on the fry below; now and then settling on an old dead overhanging limb to reconnoitre. Mill-dams are particularly visited by this feathered fisher; and the sound of his pipe is as well known to the miller as the rattling of his own hopper. Rapid streams, with high perpendicular banks, particularly if they be of a hard clayey or sandy nature, are also favourite places of resort for this bird; not only because in such places the small fish are more exposed to view, but because those steep and dry banks are the chosen situations for his nest. Into these he digs with bill and claws, horizontally, sometimes to the extent of four or five feet, at the distance of a foot or two from the surface. The few materials he takes in are not always placed at the extremity of the hole, that he and his mate may have room to turn with convenience. The eggs are five, pure white, and the first brood usually comes out about the beginning of June, and sometimes sooner, according to that part of the country where they reside. On the shores of Kentucky river, near the town of Frankfort, I found the female sitting early in April. They are very tenacious of their haunts, breeding for several successive years in the same hole, and do not readily forsake it, even though it be visited. An intelligent young gentleman informed me, that having found where a Kingsfisher built, he took away its eggs, from time to time, leaving always one behind, until he had taken no less than eighteen from the same nest. At some of these visits, the female being within, retired to the extremity of the hole while he withdrew the egg, and next day, when he returned, he found she had laid again as usual.

BUFFEL-HEADED DUCK.

ANAS ALBEOLA.

La Sarcelle de la Louisiane, BRISS. VI. *p.* 461, *pl.* 41, *fig.* 1.—*Le petit Canard à grosse téte,* BUFF. IX. *p.* 249.—EDW. *pl.* 100.—*Arct. Zool. No.* 487.—CATESBY, I. 95.—LATH. *Syn.* III. *p.* 533.—*Le Canard d'hyver,* BRISS. VI. *p.* 349; *La sarcelle de la Caroline, Id. p.* 464.—J. DOUGHTY's Collection.

THIS pretty little species, usually known by the name of the *Butter-box,* or *Butter-ball,* is common to the sea-shores, rivers and lakes of the United States, in every quarter of the country, during autumn and winter. About the middle of April, or early in May, they retire to the north to breed. They are dexterous divers, and fly with extraordinary velocity. So early as the latter part of February the males are observed to have violent disputes for the females; at this time they are more commonly seen in flocks; but during the preceding part of winter they usually fly in pairs. Their note is a short *quack.* They feed much on shell fish, shrimps, &c. They are sometimes exceedingly fat; though their flesh is inferior to many others for the table. The male exceeds the female in size, and greatly in beauty of plumage.

THE CABINET of NATURAL HISTORY AND AMERICAN RURAL SPORTS

With ILLUSTRATIONS.

VOL. III.

W.E.Tucker Sc.

T.Doughty Del.

PHILADELPHIA

Published by

John Doughty

1833

THE BEAVER.

CASTOR FIBER.

Castor Fiber, Godman, vol. ii. p. 21. Sabine, app. p. 659. Say. Long's *Expedition to the Rocky Mountains*, i. p. 464.—*Le Castor ou le Bièvre*, Briss. *Regn. an.* p. 133.—*Le Castor*, Buff. viii. pl. 36.—Philadelphia Museum.

There is no animal, native of North America, so interesting and valuable as the Beaver; and it is equally certain, that few animals of the world have been so much admired and extolled, and, at the same time, have had so large a share of intelligence imputed to them more unjustly. But, with all the importance attached to the animal, how much ignorance exists of its true character.

If we examine the opinions of men on this subject, we see at once how deeply wrong impressions have become rooted by pondering over the fictitious histories of the Beaver,—or more particularly being influenced, in early youth, by the fabulous stories of the animal, framed as truth, and admitted into the various seminaries of learning. Here we find the Beaver placed at the head of all inferior creatures for sagacity and intelligence, and endowed with intellectual qualities superior to many nations or tribes of human beings.

This undoubtedly is error, and to overturn it must be the work of time and truth, by the introduction, into schools and families, of authentic histories of the animal.

"The Beaver dams differ in shape according to the nature of the place in which they are built. If the water in the river or creek have but little motion, the dam is almost straight; but when the current is more rapid, it is always made with a considerable curve convex toward the stream. The materials made use of in those dams are drift-wood, green willows, birch, and poplars, if they can be got; also mud and stones, intermixed in such a manner as must evidently contribute to the strength of the dam; but in these dams there is no other order or method observed, except that of the work being carried on with a regular sweep, and all the parts being made of equal strength.

"The Beaver that build their houses in small rivers or creeks, in which the water is liable to be drained off when the back supplies are dried up by the frost, are wonderfully taught by instinct to provide against that evil, by making a dam quite across the river, at a convenient distance from their houses. This I look upon as the most curious piece of workmanship that is performed by the Beaver; not so much for the neatness of the work, as for its strength and real service; and at the same time it discovers such a degree of sagacity and foresight in the animal, of approaching evils, as is little inferior to that of the human species, and is certainly peculiar to those animals.

"Though the Beaver which build their houses in lakes and other standing waters, may enjoy a sufficient quantity of their favourite element without the assistance of a dam, the trouble of getting wood and other necessaries to their habitations without the help of a current, must in some measure counterbalance the other advantages which are reaped from such a situation; for it must be observed that the Beaver which build in rivers and creeks, always cut their wood above their houses, so that the current, with little trouble, conveys it to the place required.

"Those who have undertaken to describe the inside of Beaver houses, as having several apartments appropriated to various uses; such as eating, sleeping, store-houses for provisions, and one for their natural occasions, &c., must have been very little acquainted with the subject; or, which is still worse, guilty of attempting to impose on the credulous, by representing the greatest falsehoods as real facts. Many years constant residence among the Indiáns, during which I had an opportunity of seeing several hundreds of those houses, has enabled me to affirm that every thing of the kind is entirely void of truth; for, notwithstanding the sagacity of those animals, it has never been observed that they aim at any other conveniences in their houses, than to have a dry place to lie on; and there they usually eat their victuals, which they occasionally take out of the water.

"It frequently happens, that some of the large houses are found to have one or more partitions, if they deserve that appellation; but that is no more than a part of the main building, left by the sagacity of the Beaver to support the roof. On such occasions it is common for those different apartments, as some are pleased to call them, to have no communication with each other but by water; so that in fact they may be called double or treble houses, rather than different apartments of the same house. I have seen a large Beaver house built in a small island, that had near a dozen apartments under one roof: and, two or three of these only excepted, none of them had any communication with each other but by water. As there were Beaver enough to inhabit each apartment, it is more than probable that each family knew its own, and always entered at their own door, without having any further connexion with their neighbours than a friendly intercourse;

and to join their united labours in erecting their separate habitations, and building their dams where required. It is difficult to say whether their interest on other occasions was any ways reciprocal. The Indians of my party killed twelve old Beaver, and twenty-five young and half-grown ones out of the house above mentioned; and on examination found that several had escaped their vigilance, and could not be taken but at the expense of more trouble than would be sufficient to take double the number in a less difficult situation. The difficulty here alluded to, was the numberless vaults the Beaver had in the sides of the pond, and the immense thickness of the house in some parts.

"I cannot refrain from smiling, when I read the accounts of different authors who have written on the economy of those animals, as there seems to be a contest between them, who shall most exceed in fiction. But the compiler of the wonders of nature and art seems, in my opinion, to have succeeded best in this respect; as he has not only collected all the fictions into which other writers on the subject have run, but has so greatly improved on them, that little remains to be added to his account of the Beaver, beside a vocabulary of their language, a code of their laws, and a sketch of their religion, to make it the most complete natural history of that animal which can possibly be offered to the public.

"To deny that the Beaver is possessed of a very considerable degree of sagacity, would be as absurd in me, as it is in those authors who think they cannot allow them too much. I shall willingly grant them their full share; but it is impossible for any one to conceive how or by what means, a beaver, whose full height when standing erect does not exceed two feet and a half, or three feet at most, and whose fore-paws are not much larger than a half-crown piece, can 'drive stakes as thick as a man's leg into the ground three or four feet deep.' Their 'wattling those stakes with twigs,' is equally absurd; and their plaistering the inside of their houses with a composition of mud and straw, and swimming with mud and stones on their tails,' are still more incredible. The form and size of the animal, notwithstanding all its sagacity, will not admit of its performing such feats; and it would be as impossible for a beaver to use its tail as a trowel, except on the surface of the ground on which it walks, as it would have been for Sir James Thornhill to have painted the dome of St. Paul's cathedral without the assistance of scaffolding. The joints of their tail will not admit of their turning it over their backs on any occasion whatever, as it has a natural inclination to bend downwards; and it is not without some considerable exertion

that they can keep it from trailing on the ground. This being the case, they cannot sit erect like a squirrel, which is their common posture; particularly when eating, or when they are cleaning themselves, as a cat or squirrel does, without having their tails bent forward between their legs; and which may not improperly be called their trencher.

"So far are the beavers from driving stakes into the ground when building their houses, that they lay most of the wood crosswise, and nearly horizontal, and without any other order than that of leaving a hollow or cavity in the middle; when any unnecessary branches project inward, they cut them off with their teeth, and throw them in among the rest, to prevent the mud from falling through the roof. It is a mistaken notion, that the wood-work is first completed and then plaistered; for the whole of their houses, as well as their dams, are from the foundation one mass of wood and mud, mixed with stones, if they can be procured. The mud is always taken from the edge of the bank, or the bottom of the creek or pond, near the door of the house; and though their fore-paws are so small, yet it is held close up between them, under their throat, that they carry both mud and stones; while they always drag the wood with their teeth.

"With respect to the inferior, or slave-beaver, of which some authors speak, it is, in my opinion, very difficult for those who are best acquainted with the œconomy of this animal to determine whether there are any that deserve that appellation or not. It sometimes happens, that a Beaver is caught, which has but a very indifferent coat, and which has broad patches on the back, and shoulders almost wholly without hair. This is the only foundation for asserting that there is an inferior, or slave-beaver, among them. And when one of the above description is taken, it is perhaps too hastily inferred that the hair is worn off from those parts by carrying heavy loads: whereas it is most probable that it is caused by a disorder that attacks them somewhat similar to the mange; for were that falling off of the hair occasioned by performing extra labour, it is natural to think that instances of it would be more frequent than there are; as it is rare to see one of them in the course of seven or ten years. I have seen a whole house of those animals that had nothing on the surface of their bodies but the fine soft down; all the long hairs having molted off. This and every other deviation from the general run is undoubtedly owing to some particular disorder.—*Hearne's Journey to the Northern Ocean, and through the country west of Prince of Wales Fort, Hudson Bay, A. D.* 1771.

BEAVER

WILD TURKEY.

MELEAGRIS GALLOPAVO.

Meleagris Gallopavo, Ch. Bonaparte, *Synops. of Birds of the United States*, p. 122.—Ch. Bonaparte's *American Ornithology*, vol. i. p. 79, pl. IX.—Audubon's *Ornithological Biography*, p. 1, vol. i., pl. I. vol. i.

Meleagris Gallopavo, Linn. *Syst.* I. p. 268, sp. 1.—Gmel. *Syst.* I. p. 732, sp. 1.—Lath. *Ind.* p. 618, sp. 1.—Wilson, *Am. Orn.* VI. *Index*, p. xvii.—Stephens' *Cont. of* Shaw's *Zool.* XI. Part i. p. 156.

Gallopavo Sylvestris Novæ-Angliæ. a New-England Wild Turkey) Ray, *San.* p. 51, sp. 3.—Catesby *Carolina*, I. *App.* p. xliv.

Meleagris Americanus, the Wild Turkey, Bartram, *Trav.* p. 290.

Dindon, Buff. *Ois.* II. p. 132, pl. III. *Pl. Enl.* 97, *dom.*—Temm. *Hist. Nat. des Pig. et Gall.* II. p. 374.—Gerardin, *Tabl. Elem. d'Orn.* II. p. 103, pl. XXI. fig. 2.

Wild Turkey; Clayton, *Virginia, Phil. Trans.* XVII. p. 992.—Lawson, *Carolina*, p. 149.

American Turkey, Lath. *Syn.* II. Part ii. p. 676, sp. 1.

Domestic Turkey, Penn. *Brit. Zool.* I. sp. 97.—J. Doughty's collection.

The most beautiful and interesting bird of North America, is the Wild Turkey; and for usefulness, and the delicacy of its flesh, is not surpassed, if indeed equalled, by any other individual of the feathered tribe on the whole earth,—while it is a fact fully admitted, that this bird is the origin whence sprung the whole domestic race of Turkeys now scattered over almost every country.

It is not precisely known at what period the Turkey was first introduced into Europe; but from the years 1525 to 1530, the earliest mention is made of this bird,—while from that period to the present, its increase has been wonderfully rapid, until it has now become an inhabitant of almost every poultry-yard, and is regarded as a standing dish at all festivals, and tables of hotels and private families.

Many attempts have been made to introduce the Wild Turkey, in its native state, on several preserves of game in Europe,—but with the exception of one or two instances in England, they have not succeeded.

So greatly was the Turkey esteemed in Europe shortly after its introduction, that " in the year 1566, a present of twelve Turkeys was thought not unworthy of being offered by the municipality of Amiens to their king, at whose marriage, in 1570, it is stated they were first eaten in France. Heresback asserts that they were introduced into Germany about 1530; and a sumptuary law made at Venice, in 1577, particularizes the tables at which they were permitted to be served."

The following important features of the history of the Turkey, are selected from the account furnished by Mr. Audubon, who it appears has studied the habits, and written more largely, of that bird than any other natural historian.

"Turkey hens not unfrequently prefer islands for depositing their eggs and rearing their young, probably because such places are less frequented by hunters, and because the great masses of drifted timber which usually accumulate at their heads, may protect and save them in cases of great emergency.

"The mother will not leave her eggs, when near hatching, under any circumstances, while life remains. She will even allow an enclosure to be made around her, and thus suffer imprisonment, rather than abandon them. I once witnessed the hatching of a brood of Turkeys, which I watched for the purpose of securing them, together with the parent. I concealed myself on the ground within a very few feet, and saw her raise herself half the length of her legs, look anxiously upon the eggs, and cluck with a sound peculiar to the mother on such occasions, carefully remove each half-empty shell, and with her bill caress and dry the young birds, that already stood tottering and attempting to make their way out of the nest. Yes, I have seen this, and have left mother and young to better care than mine could have proved;—to the care of their Creator and mine. I have seen them all emerge from the shell, and in a few moments after, tumble, roll, and push each other forward, with astonishing and inscrutable instinct.

"Before leaving the nest with her young brood, the mother shakes herself in a violent manner, picks and adjusts the feathers about her belly, and assumes quite a different aspect. She alternately inclines her eyes obliquely upwards and sideways, stretching out her neck to discover hawks or other enemies, spreads her wings a little as she walks, and softly clucks to keep her innocent offspring close to her. They move slowly along, and as the hatching generally takes place in the afternoon, they frequently return to the nest to spend the first night there. After this, they remove to some distance, keeping on the highest undulated grounds, the mother dreading rainy weather, which is extremely dangerous to the young, in this tender state, when they are only covered by a kind of soft hairy down, of surprising delicacy.

In very rainy seasons, Turkeys are scarce, for if once completely wetted, the young seldom recover. To prevent the disastrous effects of rainy weather, the mother, like a skilful physician, plucks the buds of the spice-wood bush, and gives them to her young,

"In about a fortnight, the young birds, which had previously rested on the ground, leave it, and fly, at night, to some very large low branch, where they place themselves under the deeply-curved wings of their kind and careful parent, dividing themselves for that purpose into two nearly equal parties. After this, they leave the woods during the day, and approach the natural glades or prairies, in search of strawberries, and subsequently of dewberries, blackberries, and grasshoppers, thus obtaining abundant food, and enjoying the beneficial influence of the sun's rays. They roll themselves in deserted ants' nests, to clear their growing feathers of the loose scales, and prevent ticks and other vermin from attacking them, these insects being unable to bear the odour of the earth in which ants have been.

"About the beginning of October, when scarcely any of the seeds and fruits have yet fallen from the trees, these birds assemble in flocks, and gradually move towards the rich bottom lands of the Ohio and Mississippi. The males, or as they are more commonly called, the *gobblers*, associate in parties of from ten to a hundred, and search for food apart from the females; while the latter are seen either advancing singly, each with its brood of young, then about two-thirds grown, or in connexion with other families, forming parties often amounting to seventy or eighty individuals, all intent on shunning the old cocks, which, even when the young birds have attained this size, will fight with, and often destroy them by repeated blows on the head. Old and young, however, all move in the same course, and on foot, unless their progress be interrupted by a river, or the hunter's dog force them to take wing. When they come upon a river, they betake themselves to the highest eminences, and there often remain a whole day, or sometimes two, as if for the purpose of consultation. During this time, the males are heard *gobbling*, calling, and making much ado, and are seen strutting about, as if to raise their courage to a pitch befitting the emergency. Even the females and young assume something of the same pompous demeanour, spread out their tails and run round each other, *purring* loudly, and performing extravagant leaps. At length, when the weather appears settled, and all around is quiet, the whole party mounts to the tops of the highest trees, whence at a signal, consisting of a single *cluck*, given by a leader, the flock takes flight for the opposite shore. The old and fat birds easily get over, even should the river be a mile in breadth, but the younger and less robust, frequently fall into the water,—not to be drowned, however, as might be imagined. They bring their wings close to their body, spread out their tail as a support, stretch forward their neck, and striking out their legs with great vigour, proceed rapidly towards the shore, on approaching which, should they find it too steep for landing, they cease their exertions for a few moments, float down the stream until they come to an accessible part, and by a violent effort generally extricate themselves from the water. It is remarkable, that immediately after thus crossing a large stream, they ramble about for some time, as if bewildered. In this state, they fall an easy prey to the hunter.

"As early as the middle of February, they begin to experience the impulse of propagation. The females separate, and fly from the males. The latter strenuously pursue, and begin to gobble or to utter the notes of exultation. The sexes roost apart, but at no great distance from each other When a female utters a call-note, all the gobblers within hearing return the sound, rolling note after note with as much rapidity as if they intended to emit the last and the first together, not with spread tail, as when fluttering round the females on the ground, or practising on the branches of the trees on which they have roosted for the night, but much in the manner of the domestic Turkey, when an unusual or unexpected noise elicits its singular hubbub. If the call of the female comes from the ground, all the males immediately fly towards the spot, and the moment they reach it, whether the hen be in sight or not, spread out and erect their tail, draw the head back on the shoulders, depress their wings with a quivering motion, and strut pompously about, emitting at the same time a succession of puffs from the lungs, and stopping now and then to listen and look. But whether they spy the female or not, they continue to puff and strut, moving with as much celerity as their ideas of ceremony seem to admit. While thus occupied, the males often encounter each other, in which case desperate battles take place, ending in bloodshed, and often in the loss of many lives, the weaker falling under the repeated blows inflicted upon their head by the stronger."

WILD TURKEY

PRONG-HORNED ANTILOPE.

ANTILOPE AMERICANA.

Antilope, Lewis & Clarke, i. 75, 208, 369; ii. 169.—
Antilope Americana, Ord, Guthrie's Geography,
Philad. ed. 1815.—*Antilope Furcifer,* Smith. Trans.
of Linnæn Society, xiii. pl. 2.—*Prong-horned Ante-
lope,* Sab. App. p. 667.—*Teuthlalmaçame,* Hernan-
dez, Nov. His. p. 324, 325, Fig. 324, an. 1651.—*Le
Squenoton,* Hist. de l'Amerique, p. 175, an. 1723.—
Antilocapra Americana, Ord, Jour. de Phys. 1818.
Harlan, Fauna, p. 250.—*Cervus Hamatus,* Blain-
ville, Nouv. Bull. Societ. Phil. 1816, p. 80.—*Antilope
Palmata,* Smith, Opere Citato. Desmarest, Mam. p.
476.—*Cervus Bifurcatus,* Rafinesque.—*Apeestat-
Chœkoos,* Cree Indians.—Philadelphia Museum.

The Prong-horned Antilope, was first discovered and
described by Lewis and Clarke, while on their journey
across the Rocky Mountains. Previous to this, it was unknown to naturalists, excepting only a slight notice given
by Hernandez, of a similar animal, said to inhabit California, under the appellation of *Teuthlalmaçame.* The only
preserved specimen of the animal, existing at present in
this country, was brought by the above-mentioned gentlemen from the Missouri, and deposited in the Philadelphia
Museum.

In noticing the Prong-horned Antilope, Lewis & Clarke
give the following facts:—

" Of all the animals we had seen, the Antilope seems to
possess the most wonderful fleetness; shy and timorous,
they generally repose only on the ridges, which command
a view of all the approaches of an enemy. The acuteness
of their sight distinguishes the most distant danger, the
delicate sensibility of their smell defeats the precautions of
concealment, and when alarmed their rapid career seems
more like the flight of birds than the movements of an
earthly being. After many unsuccessful attempts, Captain
Lewis at last, by winding around the ridges, approached
a party of seven, which were on an eminence, towards
which the wind was unfortunately blowing. The only
male of the party frequently encircled the summit of the
hill, as if to announce any danger to the females, who
formed a group at the top. Although they did not see
Captain Lewis, the smell alarmed them, and they fled
when he was at the distance of two hundred yards: he
immediatuly ran to the spot where they had been, a ravine
concealed them from him, but the next moment they

appeared on a second ridge at the distance of three miles.
He doubted whether it could be the same; but their number, and the extreme rapidity with which they continued
their course, convinced him that they must have gone
with a speed equal to that of the most distinguished race-
horse.

" The Antilope inhabits the great plains of the Columbia, and resembles those found on the banks of the Missouri, and indeed in every part of the untimbered country,
but they are by no means so abundant on this as on the
other side of the Rocky Mountains. The natives make
themselves robes of their skins, and preserve the hair entire. In the summer and autumn, when the salmon begin
to decline, the majority of the natives leave the sides of the
river, and reside in the open plains, to hunt the Antilope,
which they pursue on horseback, and shoot with their
arrows."

During the last expedition to the Rocky Mountains,
under Major Long, the following incident occurred, which
eminently displays the wonderful fleetness of the Antilope.
" One afternoon, while the expedition halted, two soldiers,
mounted on excellent horses, went out to hunt. After
going some distance, they discovered, afar off, a female
Antilope, feeding on the prairie. They immediately dis-
mounted, and, after some ingenuity, succeeded in approaching sufficiently near to fire at and wound the animal,
which fled at once. They then returned to their horses,
remounted, and gave chase; but, on arriving at the spot
where the animal had been wounded, they discovered its
fawn, and as their object was diversion, they gave chase to
the fawn in preference to the wounded mother. This they
followed with the most rapid speed for upwards of two
hours, before they succeeded in making it captive, and this
was only effected, when by its exertions it sank exhausted
on the ground, and had nearly worn out the horses and
riders. The little prisoner was taken to the camp almost
lifeless, but being fed on bread and milk, it was soon revived. The next day, as the expedition was moving forward, one of the party led it by his handkerchief; but to
his surprise, instead of making any resistance, or attempts
to escape, it kept pace with his footsteps, and evinced so
much familiarity, that at length he concluded to untie it,
and see if it would follow of its own accord. This it did
for the greater part of the day, when it gave out, and was
left behind, being no doubt greatly weakened by the exertions of the previous day." From this fact, it may be
inferred, that the Antilope, if taken young, would, like the
common deer, (*Cervus Virginianus,*) leave its kind, and
abide in the habitations of man.

PRONG-HORNED ANTILOPE

RED FLAMINGO.

PHŒNICOPTERUS RUBER.

Le Flammant, BRISS. VI, *p.* 533, *pl.* 47, *fig.*1.—BUFF.
VIII, *p.* 475, *pl.* 39. *Pl. Enl.* 63.—LATH. *Syn.* III, *p.*
299.—*Arct. Zool. No.* 422.—*Phœnicopterus Baham-
ensis,* CATESBY, I, *pl.* 73, 74.—Philadelphia Museum.

The specimen from which the annexed drawing was
made, belongs to the Philadelphia Museum, and is one of
the most perfect of its kind.   This was shot by Mr. T. R.
Peale, on the sea-shore of Colombia, during his late visit
to that country, but owing to the great shyness of these
birds, he was unable to procure more than the one specimen,
although, he said, several hundreds associated together; but
the parts they resort to were so difficult of access, and the
timidity of the birds so great, rendered it impossible, without too great exertion, to be more successful.   This bird was
shot at night time by the aid of lightning, and secured only
on the following day.

American Naturalists have not been able to furnish anything new relative to this remarkable bird, and among
foreign authors, Dr. Latham, in his Synopsis, has given
the most authentic and interesting particulars, which are
here introduced.

"This remarkable bird has the neck and legs in a greater
disproportion than any other bird; the length from the end
of the bill to that of the tail is four feet two or three inches,
but to the end of the claws, measures sometimes more than
six feet.   The bill is four inches and a quarter long, and of
a construction different from that of any other bird; the
upper mandible very thin and flat, and somewhat moveable; the under thick, both of them bending downwards
from the middle; the nostrils are linear, and placed in a
blackish membrane; the end of the bill as far as the bend
is black, from thence to the base reddish yellow, round
the base quite to the eye covered with a flesh coloured
cere; the neck is slender, and of a great length; the tongue
large, fleshy, filling the cavity of the bill, furnished with
twelve or more hooked papillæ on each side, turning backwards; the tip a sharp cartilaginous substance.   The bird
when in full plumage is wholly of a most deep scarlet,
(those of Africa said to be the deepest) except the quills,
which are black; from the base of the thigh to the claws
measures thirty-two inches, of which the feathered part
takes up no more than three inches; the bare part above
the knee thirteen inches, and from thence to the claws
sixteen; the colour of the bare parts is red, and the toes
are furnished with a web as in the duck genus; but it is
deeply indented. *The legs are not straight, but slightly
bent, the shin rather projecting.*

"These birds do not gain their full plumage till the
third year.   In the first they are of a grayish white for the
most part; the second of a clearer white, tinged with red,
or rather rose colour; but the wings and scapulars are red;
in the third year a general glowing scarlet manifests itself
throughout; the bill and legs also keep pace with the gra-
dation of colour in the plumage, these parts changing to
their colours by degrees as the bird approaches to an adult
state.

"Flamingoes, for the most part, keep together in flocks;
and now and then are seen in great numbers together, except in breeding time.   Dampier mentions having, with
two more in company, killed fourteen at once; but this
was effected by secreting themselves; for they are very
shy birds, and will by no means suffer any one to approach
openly near enough to shoot them.‡   Kolben observes
that they are very numerous at the Cape, keeping in the
day on the borders of the lakes and rivers, and lodging
themselves of nights in the long grass on the hills.   They
are also common to various places in the warmer parts of
America, frequenting the same latitudes as in other quarters of the world; being met with in Peru, Chili, Cayenne,§
and the coast of Brazil, as well as the various islands of
the West Indies.   Sloane found them in Jamaica; but particularly at the Bahama islands, and that of Cuba, where
they breed.   When seen at a distance they appear as a re-
giment of soldiers, being arranged alongside of one another,
on the borders of the rivers, searching for food, which
chiefly consists of small fish, or the eggs of them, and of
water insects, which they search after by plunging in the
bill and part of the head; from time to time trampling with
their feet to muddy the water, that their prey may be
raised from the bottom.   In feeding are said to twist the
neck in such a manner that the upper part of the bill is
applied to the ground; during this, one of them is said to
stand sentinel, and the moment he sounds the alarm, the
whole flock take wing.   This bird when at rest stands on
one leg, the other being drawn up close to the body, with
the head placed under the wing on that side of the body
it stands on.

"The flesh of these birds is esteemed pretty good meat;
and the young thought by some equal to that of a partridge;
but the greatest dainty is the tongue, which was esteemed
by the ancients an exquisite morsel.   Are sometimes caught
young and brought up tame; but are ever impatient of cold,
and in this state will seldom live a great while, gradually
losing their colour, flesh, and appetite; and dying for want
of that food which in a state of nature, at large, they were
abundantly supplied with."

‡ Davies talks of the gunner disguising himself in an ox hide, and by this
means getting within gun-shot. Hist. Barbad. p. 88.

§ Called there by the name of Tococo.

RED FLAMINGO

INDIGO BIRD

GOLDEN-WINGED WARBLER

GOLDEN-WINGED WARBLER.

SYLVIA CHRYSOPTERA.

Edw. 299.—*Le figuier aux ailes dorees*, Buff. v. 311.—
Lath. ii. 492.—*Arct. Zool.* 403, *No.* 295. *Ib.- No.*
296.—*Motacilla chrysoptera*, Turt. *Syst.* i. 597.—
Motacilla flavifrons, Yellow-fronted Warbler, Id.
601.—*Parus alis aureis*, Bartram, *p.* 292.—*Motacilla chrysoptera*, Linn. *Syst.* i. p. 333.—Gmel. Syst.
i. p. 971.—*Motacilla flavifrons*, Gmel. Syst. i. p. 976.
—*Sylvia chrysoptera*, Lath. *Ind. Orn.* ii. p. 541.—
Vieill. *Ois. de l'Am. Sept. pl.* 97. *Sylvia flavifrons*,
Lath. *Ind. Orn.* ii. p. 527.—Collection of L. J. Salaignac, Esq.

[On a branch of Dog-wood.]

This is another spring passenger through the United
States to the north. This bird, from the particular form of
its bill, ought rather to be separated from the Warblers,
or, along with several others of the same kind, might be
arranged as a sub genus, or particular family of that tribe,
which might with propriety be called *Wormeaters*, the
Motacilla vermivora of Turton, having the bill exactly
of this form. The habits of these birds partake a good
deal of those of the Titmouse, and in their language and
action they very much resemble them. All that can be
said of this species is, that it appears in Pennsylvania for a
few days, about the last of April or beginning of May,
darting actively among the young leaves and opening buds,
and is rather a scarce species.

INDIGO BIRD.

FRINGILLA CYANEA.

Tanagra cyanea, Linn. *Syst.* i. 315.—*Le Ministre*,
Buffon, iv. 96.—*Indigo Bunting, Arct. Zool.* ii. No.
235.—Lath. *Syn.* iii. 205, 63.—*Blue Linnet*, Edw.
273.—*Linaria cyanea*, Bartram, p. 290.—Collection
of L. J. Salaignac, Esq.

[On a branch of Dog-wood.]

This is another of those rich-plumaged tribes, that visit

us in spring from the regions of the south. It arrives in
Pennsylvania on the second week in May, and disappears
about the middle of September. It is numerous in all the
settled parts of the middle and eastern states; in the Carolinas and Georgia it is also abundant. Though Catesby
says that it is only found at a great distance from the sea;
yet round the city of New-York, and in many places along
the shores of New-Jersey, I have met with them in plenty.
I may also add, on the authority of Mr. William Bartram,
that "they inhabit the continent and sea-coast islands,
from Mexico to Nova-Scotia, from the sea-coast west beyond the Apalachian and Cherokee mountains." They
are also known in Mexico, where they probably winter.
Its favourite haunts, while with us, are about gardens,
fields of deep clover, the borders of woods, and road
sides, where it is frequently seen perched on the fences.
In its manners it is extremely active and neat; and a
vigorous and pretty good songster. It mounts to the highest tops of a large tree, and chants for half an hour at a
time. Its song is not one continued strain, but a repetition of short notes, commencing loud and rapid, and falling by almost imperceptible gradations for six or eight
seconds, till they seem hardly articulate, as if the little
minstrel were quite exhausted; and after a pause of half a
minute or less commences again as before. Some of our
birds sing only in spring, and then chiefly in the morning,
being comparatively mute during the heat of noon; but
the Indigo bird chants with as much animation under the
meridian sun, in the month of July, as in the month of
May; and continues his song, occasionally, to the middle
or end of August. His usual note, when alarmed by an
approach to his nest, is a sharp *chip*, like that of striking
two hard pebbles smartly together.

Notwithstanding the beauty of his plumage, the vivacity
with which he sings, and the ease with which he can be
reared and kept, the Indigo bird is seldom seen domesticated. The few I have met with were taken in trapcages; and such of any species rarely sing equal to those
which have been reared by hand from the nest. There is
one singularity, which as it cannot be well represented in
the figure, may be mentioned here, viz. that in some certain lights his plumage appears of a rich sky-blue, and in
others of a vivid verdigrise green;* so that the same bird, in
passing from one place to another before your eyes, seems
to undergo a total change of colour. When the angle of
incidence of the rays of light, reflected from his plumage,
is acute, the colour is green, when obtuse, blue. Such I
think I have observed to be uniformly the case, without being
optician enough to explain why it is so. From this, however, must be excepted the colour of the head, which being
of a very deep blue, is not affected by a change of position.

BALTIMORE ORIOLE

CHESTNUT-SIDED WARBLER

CHESNUT-SIDED WARBLER.

SYLVIA PENNSYLVANICA.

LINN. *Syst.* 333.—*Red-throated Flycatcher*, EDW. 301.—
Bloody-side Warbler, TURTON, *Syst.* I. p. 596.—*La
figuier a poitrine rouge*, BUFF. V. 308.—BRISS. *App.*
105.—LATH. II. 490.—*Arct. Zool.* p. 405. No. 298.—
Motacilla icterocephala, LINN. *Syst.* I. p. 325.—GMEL.
Syst. I. p. 980.—*Sylvia icterocephala*, LATH. *Ind. Orn.*
II. p. 538.—VIEIL. *Ois. de l'Am. Sept. pl.* 90.—*Sylvia
Pennsylvanica*, GMEL. *Syst.* I. p. 971.—LATH. *Ind.
Orn.* II. p. 540.—*Ficedula Canadensis icterocephalas*,
BRISS. III. p. 517, 64, *t.* 27, *f.* 2.—*Id.* 8vo. I. p. 451.—
Ficedula Pennsylvanica icterocephalas, BRISS. *App.* p.
105.—*Id.* 8vo. I. p. 458, 78.—Collection of L. J. SA-
LAIGNAC, Esq.

OF this bird I can give but little account. It is one of
those transient visitors that pass through Pennsylvania in
April and May, on their way farther north to breed.
During its stay here, which seldom exceeds a week or ten
days, it appears actively engaged among the opening buds
and young leaves, in search of insects; has no song but a
feeble chirp or twitter, and is not numerous. As it leaves
us early in May, it probably breeds in Canada, or perhaps
some parts of New-England, though I have no certain
knowledge of the fact. In a whole day's excursion, it is
rare to meet with more than one or two of these birds,
though a thousand individuals of some species may be seen
in the same time. Perhaps they may be more numerous
in some other parts of the continent.

Turton, and some other writers, have bestowed on this
little bird the singular epithet of *bloody-sided*, for which I
was at a loss to know the reason, the colour of that part
being a plain chesnut; till on examining Mr. Edwards's
coloured figure of this bird in the public library of this
city, I found its side tinged with a brilliant blood colour.
Hence, I suppose, originated the name!—WILSON.

BALTIMORE ORIOLE.

ICTERUS BALTIMORUS.

LINN. *Syst.* I. p. 162, 10.—*Icterus minor*, BRISS. II. p.
109, *pl.* 12., *fig.* 1.—*Le Baltimore*, BUFF. III. p. 231.
Pl. Enl. 506, *fig.* 1.—*Baltimore Bird*, CATESB. *Car.*
1, 48.—*Arct. Zool.* II. p. 142.—LATH. *Syn.* II. p. 432,
19, BARTRAM, p. 290.—Collection of L. J. SALAIGNAC,
Esq.

THIS is a bird of passage, arriving in Pennsylvania,
from the south, about the beginning of May, and departing
towards the latter end of August, or beginning of September. From the singularity of its colours, the construction
of its nest, and its preferring the apple-trees, weeping-
willows, walnut and tulip-trees, adjoining the farm-house,
to build on, it is generally known, and, as usual, honored
with a variety of names, such as Hang-nest, Hanging-bird,
Golden Robin, Fire-bird, (from the bright orange seen
through the green leaves, resembling a flash of fire,) &c.
but more generally the Baltimore-bird, so named, as
Catesby informs us, from its colours, which are black and
orange, being those of the arms or livery of Lord Baltimore, formerly proprietary of Maryland.

Almost the whole genus of Orioles belong to America,
and with a few exceptions build pensile nests. Few of
them, however, equal the Baltimore in the construction of
these receptacles for their young, and in giving them, in
such a superior degree, convenience, warmth, and security. For these purposes he generally fixes on the high
bending extremities of the branches, fastening strong
strings of hemp or flax round two forked twigs, corresponding to the intended width of the nest; with the same materials, mixed with quantities of loose tow, he interweaves
or fabricates a strong firm kind of cloth, not unlike the
substance of a hat in its raw state, forming it into a pouch
of six or seven inches in depth, lining it substantially with
various soft substances, well interwoven with the outward
netting, and lastly, finishes with a layer of horse hair; the
whole being shaded from the sun and rain by a natural pent-house, or canopy of leaves. As to a hole being
left in the side for the young to be fed, and void their ex-
crements through, as Pennant and others relate, it is certainly an error: I have never met with any thing of the
kind in the nest of the Baltimore.

So solicitous is the Baltimore to procure proper materials for his nest, that, in the season of building, the women
in the country are under the necessity of narrowly watching their thread that may chance to be out bleaching, and
the farmer to secure his young grafts; as the Baltimore,
finding the former, and the strings which tie the latter, so
well adapted for his purpose, frequently carries off both; or
should the one be too heavy, and the other too firmly tied,
he will tug at them a considerable time before he gives up
the attempt. Skeins of silk, and hanks of thread, have
been often found, after the leaves were fallen, hanging
round the Baltimore's nest; but so woven up, and entangled, as to be entirely irreclaimable.

DEATH OF THE FOX

FOX HUNTING.

DEATH OF THE FOX.

The morn is rising bright and red,
(As Venus blushed from Neptune's bed,)
And throwing by her dusky veil,
Descends into the lowland dale.
Light mist-wreaths round her forehead curl,
Her neck is gemmed with liquid pearl;
And hosts of fragrant flowers display
Their beauties in her shining way.
The radiant stars that came with night
   To sing the chorus of the sky,
Now " pale their ineffectual" light,
   Before the day-god's beaming eye,
And shrinking one by one away,
   Leave the blue vault without a stain,
With here and there a cloud to stray
   Like lonely wanderers o'er the plain.
The rosy tinge that marks the east
   With beauty art can never show,
With morning's rise is still increased,
   Until it breaks into one glow
Of rich and burning golden light,
Too glorious for the dazzled sight.

How still is all the sleeping earth !
   And not a sound in heaven is heard,
Save now and then a note of mirth
   Bursting from some awakening bird,

That in the ecstacy of life,
   Up from its leafy quiet springs,
And with its mate in lovely strife,
   Soars in the joyous beam, and sings.

All else is silent as the night,
   And breathless as the early dew,
That sleeps in drops of glittering light
   Upon the wild flowers rosy hue.

Frail things of earth that spring to life,
   And drink the sun, and shine and die—
And yet with being's glory rife,
   Are wonderful to human eye.

But hark !—a distant sound I hear,
It comes like music on mine ear—
Again !—it is the bugle's note,
   Borne on the misty air along—
It seems upon the breeze to float
   As if some spirit woke its song.
Again it breathes—and nearer now—
   A louder and a clearer strain—
And echo answers soft and low,
   As though she deemed her effort vain.

O ! at the hour of early morn,
   Earth has no such inspiring sound,
As that of the resounding horn
   That wakes the silence all around.
How sweetly on the ear it thrills,

Bounding from o'er the distant hills,
Bearing the mind in fancy back
To chaste Diana's rosy track,
When thro' the summer woods she flew,
And scarce disturbed the honey'd dew.

But louder now the echoes swell—
And hark ! I hear the distant yell
Of eager hounds that scent their prey
Thro' fields and fallow far away—
They come—they come—the clam'rous pack
   Lifting their voices in full cry,
And close upon the fox's track,
   Like mountain-torrent, they sweep by—
And horse and huntsman follow near,
   Dashing thro' ditch, thro' briar and brake
He strikes the spur, the bank they clear—
   The whip is raised, they swim the lake.

Away—away—with careless speed,
   Strained to the task, they onward bound—
Away—away—go man and steed—
   Away—away—go horn and hound.

The wearied prey begins to faint,
   He turns and doubles, all in vain—
The eager dogs defy restraint,
   And hunt him to the open plain.

But safer 'mid the sheltering trees,
   Back to the woods he speeds his way,
Yet still his scent is on the breeze,
   And yelling hounds pursue their prey.

In vain he strives, with swifter pace,
   To leave his ravening foes behind—
In vain he would their scent misplace,
   And bid them snuff the vacant wind.

In vain his toil—in vain his care—
   For bursting in with furious sound,
Like thunder on the summer air,
   His fierce pursuers close him round.

From front to rear the gathering clan
   Send their proud echo to the skies—
And 'mid the shouts of brute and man,
   At length the hapless victim dies.

The early mists have rolled away,
   And high in heaven careers the sun—
While in the face of garish day,
   The horn proclaims the conquest won.

O did we take for heaven above,
   (So sings the bard of melody,)
The pains we take for woman's love,
   What very angels should we be.
O did we run our better race,
   (Thus may the muse conclude her strain,)
With half the zeal we give the chase,
   What endless honours should we gain.

SPOTTED GROUSE

SPOTTED GROUS.

TETRAO CANADENSIS.

[half size.]

Tetrao Canadensis, Ch. BONAPARTE's *American Ornithology*, Vol. III. p. 47, *pl.* XXI.—LINN, *Syst.* I. p. 207. *sp.* 3.—GMEL. *Syst.* I. p. 749, *sp.* 3.—LATH. *Ind.* p. 637, *sp.* 6.—FORSTER, *in Phil. Trans.* LXII. p. 389.— TEMM. *Ind. Gall. in Hist. Pig. et Gall.* III. p. 702.— VIEILL. *Novio. Dict. Hist. Nat.*—SABINE, *Zool. app. Frank. Exp.* p. 683.—NOB. *Cat. birds, U. S. sp.* 207. ID. *Syn. Birds, U. S. sp.* 108.
Lagopus Bonasa Freti Hudsonis, BRISS. *Orn.* I. p. 201. *sp.* 6.—KLEIN. *Av.* p. 117, *sp.* 6.—*La Gelinotte du Canada*, BUFF. *Ois.* II. p. 279.—*Black and Spotted Heath Cock*, EDW. *Glean. p.* 71, *pl.* 118.—*Brown and Spotted Heath Cock*, ELLIS. *Hudson Bay*, I. *t.* p. 50.
Spotted Grous, PENN. *Arct. Zool. sp.* 182, LATH. *Syn.* IV. p. 735, *sp.* 6. *In Suppl.* p. 214.—*The small Speckled Pheasant*, LEWIS *and* CLARK *Exp.* II. p. 182. —Philadelphia Museum.

" THE Spotted Grous," says M. Bonaparte, " is well characterized by its much rounded tail of but sixteen broad and rounded feathers, and may at once distinguished from all others by the large and conspicuous white spots, ornamenting the breast, flanks, and under tail-coverts.

" It has been inaccurately compared with the European *Tetrao bonasia*, from which it differs very materially, not even being of the same subgenus, and approaching nearer, if indeed it can be compared with any, to the *Tetrao urogallus*.

" This bird is common at Hudson's Bay throughout the year—there frequenting the plains and low grounds, though in other parts of America it is found on mountains, even of great elevation. It inhabits Canada in winter, and was seen by Vieillot in great numbers, during the month of October, in Nova Scotia. Lewis and Clark met with it on the elevated range of the Rocky Mountains, and brought back from their western expedition a male specimen, now deposited in the Philadelphia Museum, where it has been long exhibited under the name of Louisiana Grous. This, as truly observed by Say, first entitled it to rank among birds of the United States. But the Rocky Mountains are not the only region of the United States territory where the Spotted Grous is found. We have traced it with certainty as a winter visitant of the northern extremity of Maine, Michigan, and even the state of New-York; where, though very rare, it is found in the counties of Lewis and Jefferson. On the frontiers of Maine it is abundant, and has been seen by Professor Holmes of the Gardiner Lyceum, near Lake Umbagog, and others. In these countries the Spotted Grous is known by the various names of Wood Partridge, Swamp Partridge, Cedar Partridge, and Spruce Partridge. The American settlers of Canada distinguish it by the first. In Michigan and New-York it generally goes by the second. In Maine it bears the third ; and in other parts of New-England, New-Brunswick, &c., more properly the last. We have been informed by Gen. Henry A. S. Dearborn, that they are sent from Nova Scotia and New-Brunswick to Boston in a frozen state ; as in the north they are known to be so kept hanging throughout the winter, and when wanted for use, they need only be taken down and placed in cold water to thaw. General Dearborn, to whom we are much indebted for the information which his interest for science has induced him voluntarily to furnish, mentions, that he has heard from his father, during the progress of the expedition under Arnold through the wilderness to Quebec in 1775, these Grous were occasionally shot between the tide waters of the Kennebeck river, and the sources of the Chaudiere, now forming part of the state of Maine. Five specimens of the Spotted Grous have been sent to the Lyceum of Natural History of New-York from the Sault de ste Marie, by Mr. Schoolcraft, whose exertions in availing himself of the opportunities which his residence affords him for the advancement of every branch of Zoology, merits the highest praise. He informs us that this bird is common from Lake Huron to the sources of the Mississippi, being called in the Chipeway language Mushcodasee, i. e. Partridge of the Plains.

" The favourite haunts of the Spotted Grous are pine woods, and dark cedar swamps ; in winter resorting to the deep forests of spruce to feed on the tops and leaves of these ever-greens, as well as on the seeds contained in their cones, and on juniper berries. Hence their flesh, though at all times good, is much better in summer, as in winter it has a strong flavour of spruce. At Hudson's Bay, where they are called indifferently Wood or Spruce Partridge, they are seen throughout the year. Like other Grous, they build on the ground, laying perhaps seven eggs; these are white, yellow, and black. They are easily approached, being unsuspicious, and by no means so shy as the common Ruffed Grous, and are killed or trapped in numbers without much artifice being necessary for this purpose. When much disturbed, like their kindred species, they are apt to resort to trees, where, by using the precaution of always shooting the lowest, the whole terrified flock may be brought down to the last bird."

DATA APPEARING ON PLATES

Nineteen hundred and fifty copies of this book have been printed by The Meriden Gravure Company for the IMPRINT Society from a set of original issues belonging to the Beinecke Rare Book and Manuscript Library at Yale University. Design is by Raymond M. Grimaila, composition by The Eastern Typesetting Company and the binding is by A. Horowitz & Son, Bookbinders. The paper is Imprint Society Text from the Monadnock Mills, Inc.

This is copy number

1049